Sir William Osler

A Selection

SIR WILLIAM OSLER

1849 – 1919

William Osler in 1881

Sir William Osler

1849–1919

A Selection
for Medical Students

Edited
and with an Introduction by
Charles G. Roland

The Hannah Institute for the History of Medicine
Toronto

Canadian Cataloguing in Publication Data
Osler, William, Sir, 1849–1919.
  Sir William Osler, 1849–1919 : a selection for
medical students

ISBN 0–7720–1341–1

1. Medicine – Addresses, essays, lectures.
2. Medical education – Addresses, essays, lectures.
I. Roland, Charles G., 1933-   II. Hannah Institute
for the History of Medicine.   III. Title.

R708.084   610   C82–094397–5

©1982 The Hannah Institute for the History of Medicine.
Published for The Hannah Institute for the History of
Medicine by Irwin Publishing Inc.

ISBN 0–7720–1341–1

2 3 4 5   JD   89 88 87 86

Printed in Canada

CONTENTS

Preface   vii

Introduction: Sir William Osler   ix

Aequanimitas (1889)   1

The Fixed Period (1905)   9

The Student Life (1905)   27

A Backwood Physiologist (1902)   49

The Growth of a Profession (1885)   75

The Historical Development and Relative
    Value of Laboratory and Clinical Methods
    in Diagnosis (1907)   103

A Note on the Teaching of the
History of Medicine (1902)   112

Postscript   115

Bibliography   116

Preface

The idea that a book of Osleriana should be compiled and presented to Ontario medical students originated in an annual meeting of the Hannah Professors of the History of Medicine. They recommended that Associated Medical Services, Inc., the parent of the Hannah Institute for the History of Medicine and the funding source for the five Hannah Chairs, should produce such a book, the contents of which would be selected by Dr. Charles G. Roland, Hannah Professor at McMaster University, in consultation with his colleagues.

The Board of Directors of Associated Medical Services, Inc. has been pleased to accept the recommendation of the Hannah Professors and acknowledges gratefully the special role of Professor Roland in this project.

It is our belief that Ontario medical students will find this sampling of Osler's writings interesting, challenging and pertinent to many of the questions that will arise in their minds as they mature in the practice of their noble profession. Osler's lifelong interest in students, in libraries, and in the history of medicine are apparent in his writings. It is hoped that these and his other fine qualities may influence the readers of this selection.

This book is dedicated to Sir William Osler and to Ontario practitioners of medicine.

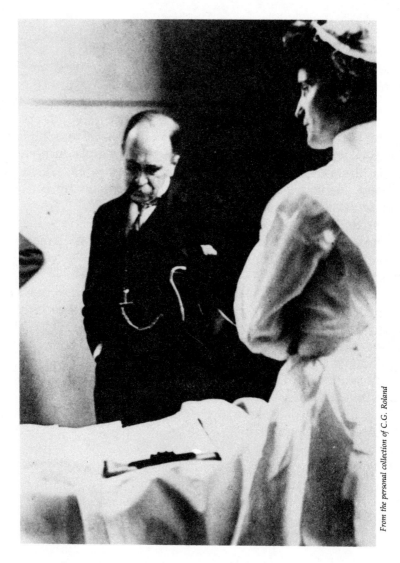

Osler on the wards at Johns Hopkins, c. 1904

Sir William Osler

William Osler was born in 1849, at Bond Head, Ontario, to parents who had emigrated from England a dozen years before. His father was minister to the Church of England souls in that area until the need to obtain adequate schooling for his nine children, of whom Will was the second youngest, took the family to Dundas when Will was eight. That town was his family home for years, though he attended two boarding schools before entering the University of Toronto in 1867, originally intending to follow his father into the ministry.

However, through the teaching and example of two men — a clergyman and a physician — William had discovered the microscope, and through it nature and science. Divinity was abandoned for medicine, which he studied for two years in Toronto and a further two years at McGill, graduating M.D. with distinction in 1872. After two years spent acquiring an informal postgraduate education in Europe, Osler returned to Canada, first doing some *locum tenens* work in Dundas and Hamilton but soon accepting an invitation to teach at McGill. From 1874 to 1884, Osler taught medical and veterinary students, performed autopsies, cared for thousands of ward patients and a small private practice, and wrote insightful accounts of his work in various journals.

By 1884, his reputation had expanded rapidly; in that year he was elected a fellow of the Royal College of Physicians. Despite efforts to keep him in Montreal, he accepted an invitation to the University of Pennsylvania, from where, only five years later, he was selected to be the first head of medicine at Johns Hopkins Hospital and the medical school there. At Hopkins, where he remained from 1889 till 1905, he earned an international reputation as a brilliant clinician and teacher involved in innovative approaches to medical education. The Johns Hopkins clinic linked the academic study of medicine to the functioning hospital, making practical training central to the curriculum of medical students. In 1892 Osler published the first edition of his renowned text, *The Principles and Practice of Medicine*, a lucid and literate work that would have an enormous influence on medicine for over forty years.

By 1905, Osler was so overworked that he accepted the invitation of King Edward VII (on the recommendation of the British Prime Minister) to become Regius Professor of Medicine at Oxford University in England, the highest medical position in Great Britain, though a relatively quiet situation clinically. He moved to Oxford with Grace, his wife of thirteen years, and their nine-year-old son Revere, and was created a Baronet in 1911. For the final fourteen years of his life Osler revised his text repeatedly, and continued to write clinical articles, historical essays, and the "lay sermons" with which his name is so closely associated.

At the time of his death, in 1919, still grief-stricken over the loss of his only son in Flanders two years before, Sir William was without question the best known and best loved physician in the English-speaking world. He remained closely bound to Canada, never relinquishing his citizenship. His family are here still, and he had many close friends across the country. In his will he bequeathed his magnificent historical library to McGill University, where it has been a focus of historical medical scholarship for over half a century.

Osler influenced innumerable men and women throughout his lifetime, perhaps none more than medical students. He liked students, and they liked him, flocking to his lectures and clinics, competing for places in his hospital entourage, and copying down, with admiration, not only his clinical insights but also his bon mots on all subjects. He offered special voluntary classes in microscopy at McGill, at a time when the microscope was rarely used in medical teaching in North America. The Osler home — whether his bachelor apartments in Montreal and Philadelphia or his houses in Baltimore and Oxford — was open to students as well as to interns, residents and professional colleagues. With great appropriateness, his Oxford mansion was nicknamed "The Open Arms." As a teacher, Osler had an uncanny knack for pushing bright students into areas of study that so engrossed them that lifetime vocations often resulted. For these reasons, and many more, it has seemed apt to re-issue some of Osler's essays for the particular use of medical students.

Those who persevere will learn something of William Osler's outlook on medical practice, on medical education, and on medical history. I would hope it will also become evident that he saw these three aspects of our professional lives as interrelated and, indeed, as co-dependent. Some readers stumble over Osler's style, a reaction that most likely stems from his generous use of allusion to (and quotation from) classical writings of all kinds, most particularly the Bible, Greek and Latin prose and poetry, and the works of Shakespeare and Emerson. On this continent, our educational system has long since abandoned any pretence of providing a solid classical background to all its students (or even to any substantial proportion of them), so that such allusions can be distracting to modern readers. This potential difficulty aside, the six essays and the letter-to-the-editor contain many well written, stimulating passages that present messages by no means stale or hackneyed. Certainly the common sense advice of "Aequanimitas" can benefit us all.

Because Osler's own bibliography exceeds 1500 items, this anthology must omit many fine works. For those who wish to read more about or by Osler, a short, basic bibliography follows the text. The essays which have been selected give a range of his exhortatory and historical writings, as well as a range in their author's age, being written variously from the ages of thirty-six through fifty-eight.

Teaching and research in the history of medicine did not acquire a genuine professional base in North America until the second decade after Osler's death. Nevertheless, he saw clearly both the humanistic and the practical advantages of knowledge of our profession's origins and he acted on his belief, taking opportunities regularly to present an historical view. He did this in many ways, some of which are exemplified in the three historical essays in this collection, while others are described in the final brief letter.

If you, the reader, are stimulated to further interest in these non-technical aspects of medicine — areas that can suffer from curricular squeezes in the best-run schools — then this small anthology will have served its purpose well.

Charles G. Roland, M.D.
Jason A. Hannah Professor
of the History of Medicine
McMaster University, Hamilton,Ontario

William Osler

AEQUANIMITAS*

"Aequanimitas" was first published as a pamphlet in the year the address was delivered (Philadelphia, W.F. Fell & Co., 1889), and was the title essay of Osler's anthology, Aequanimitas, with other Addresses to Medical Students, Nurses and Practitioners of Medicine, *first published in 1904 and frequently since. (London, H.K. Lewis; Philadelphia, P. Blakiston's Sons & Co.).*

TO many the frost of custom has made even these imposing annual ceremonies cold and lifeless. To you, at least of those present, they should have the solemnity of an ordinance—called as you are this day to a high dignity and to so weighty an office and charge. You have chosen your Genius, have passed beneath the Throne of Necessity, and with the voices of the fatal sisters still in your ears, will soon enter the plain of Forgetfulness and drink of the waters of its river. Ere you are driven all manner of ways, like the souls in the tale of Er the Pamphylian,** it is my duty to say a few words of encouragement and to bid you, in the name of the Faculty, God-speed on your journey.

I could have the heart to spare you, poor, careworn survivors of a hard struggle, so "lean and pale and leaden-eyed with study"; and my tender mercy constrains me to consider but two of the score of elements which may make or mar your lives—which may contribute to your success, or help you in the days of failure.

In the first place, in the physician or surgeon no quality takes rank with imperturbability, and I propose for a few minutes to

* Valedictory Address, University of Pennsylvania, May 1, 1889.
** *The Republic,* Book X.

direct your attention to this essential bodily virtue. Perhaps I may be able to give those of you, in whom it has not developed during the critical scenes of the past month, a hint or two of its importance, possibly a suggestion for its attainment. Imperturbability means coolness and presence of mind under all circumstances, calmness amid storm, clearness of judgment in moments of grave peril, immobility, impassiveness, or, to use an old and expressive word, *phlegm*. It is the quality which is most appreciated by the laity though often misunderstood by them; and the physician who has the misfortune to be without it, who betrays indecision and worry, and who shows that he is flustered and flurried in ordinary emergencies, loses rapidly the confidence of his patients.

In full development, as we see it in some of our older colleagues, it has the nature of a divine gift, a blessing to the possessor, a comfort to all who come in contact with him. You should know it well, for there have been before you for years several striking illustrations, whose example has, I trust, made a deep impression. As imperturbability is largely a bodily endowment, I regret to say that there are those amongst you, who, owing to congenital defects, may never be able to acquire it. Education, however, will do much; and with practice and experience the majority of you may expect to attain to a fair measure. The first essential is to have your nerves well in hand. Even under the most serious circumstances, the physician or surgeon who allows "his outward action to demonstrate the native act and figure of his heart in complement extern," who shows in his face the slightest alteration, expressive of anxiety or fear, has not his medullary centres under the highest control, and is liable to disaster at any moment. I have spoken of this to you on many occasions, and have urged you to educate your nerve centres so that not the slightest dilator or contractor influence shall pass to the vessels of your face under any professional trial. Far be it from me to urge you, ere Time has carved with his hours those fair brows, to quench on all occasions the blushes of ingenuous shame, but in dealing with your patients emergencies demanding these should certainly not arise, and at other times an inscrutable face may prove a fortune. In a true and perfect form, imperturbability is indissolubly associated with wide experience and an intimate knowledge of the varied aspects of disease. With such advantages he is so equipped that no eventuality can disturb the mental equilibrium of the physician; the possibilities are always manifest, and the course of action clear. From its very nature this precious quality is liable to be misinterpreted, and the general accusation of hardness, so often brought against the profession, has here its foundation. Now a certain measure of insensibility is not only an advantage, but a positive necessity in the exercise of a calm judgment, and in carrying out delicate operations. Keen sensibility is doubtless a virtue of high order, when it does not interfere with steadiness of hand or coolness of nerve; but for the practitioner in his working-day world, a callousness which thinks only of the good to be effected, and goes ahead regardless of smaller considerations, is the preferable quality.

Cultivate, then, gentlemen[1], such a judicious measure of obtuseness as will enable you to meet the exigencies of practice with firmness and courage, without, at the same time, hardening "the human heart by which we live."

In the second place, there is a mental equivalent to this bodily endowment, which is as important in our pilgrimage as imperturbability. Let me recall to your minds an incident related of that best of men and wisest of rulers, Antoninus Pius, who, as he lay dying, in his home at Lorium in Etruria, summed up the philosophy of life in the watchword, *Aequanimitas*. As for him, about to pass *flammantia moenia mundi* (the flaming ramparts of the world), so for you, fresh from Clotho's spindle, a calm equanimity is the desirable attitude. How difficult to attain, yet how necessary, in success as in failure! Natural temperament has much to do with its development, but a clear knowledge of our relation to our fellow-creatures and to the work of life is also indispensable. One of the first essentials in securing a good-natured equanimity is not to expect too much of the people amongst whom you dwell. "Knowledge comes, but wisdom lingers," and in matters medical the ordinary citizen of to-day has not one whit more sense than the old Romans, whom Lucian scourged for a credulity which made them fall easy victims to the quacks of the time, such as the notorious Alexander, whose exploits make one wish that his advent had been delayed some eighteen centuries. Deal gently then with this deliciously credulous old human nature in which we work, and restrain your indignation, when you find your pet parson has triturates of the 1000th potentiality in his waistcoat pocket,[2] or you discover accidentally a case of Warner's Safe Cure in the bedroom of your best patient. It must needs be that offences of this kind come; expect them, and do not be vexed.

Curious, odd compounds are these fellow-creatures, at whose mercy you will be; full of fads and eccentricities, of whims and fancies; but the more closely we study their little foibles of one sort and another in the inner life which we see, the more surely is the conviction borne in upon us of the likeness of their weaknesses to our own. The similarity would be intolerable, if a happy egotism did not often render us forgetful of it. Hence the need of an infinite patience and of an ever-tender charity toward these fellow-creatures; have they not to exercise the same toward us?

A distressing feature in the life which you are about to enter, a feature which will press hardly upon the finer spirits among you and ruffle their equanimity, is the uncertainty which pertains not alone to our science and art, but to the very hopes and fears which make us men. In seeking absolute truth we aim at the unattainable, and must be content with finding broken portions. You remember in the Egyptian story, how Typhon with his conspirators dealt with good Osiris; how they took the virgin Truth, hewed her lovely form into a thousand pieces, and scattered them to the four winds; and, as Milton says, "from that time ever since, the sad friends of truth, such as durst appear, imitating the careful search that Isis made for the mangled body of Osiris, went up and down gathering up limb by limb still as they could find them. We have not yet found them all,* "but each one of us may pick up a fragment, perhaps two, and in moments when mortality weighs less heavily upon the spirit, we can, as in a vision, see the form divine, just as

* *Areopagitica.*

a great Naturalist, an Owen or a Leidy, can reconstruct an ideal creature from a fossil fragment.

It has been said that in prosperity our equanimity is chiefly exercised in enabling us to bear with composure the misfortunes of our neighbours. Now, while nothing disturbs our mental placidity more sadly than straightened means, and the lack of those things after which the Gentiles seek, I would warn you against the trials of the day soon to come to some of you—the day of large and successful practice. Engrossed late and soon in professional cares, getting and spending, you may so lay waste your powers that you may find, too late, with hearts given away, that there is no place in your habit-stricken souls for those gentler influences which make life worth living.

It is sad to think that, for some of you, there is in store disappointment, perhaps failure. You cannot hope, of course, to escape from the cares and anxieties incident to professional life. Stand up bravely, even against the worst. Your very hopes may have passed on out of sight, as did all that was near and dear to the Patriarch at the Jabbok ford, and, like him, you may be left to struggle in the night alone. Well for you, if you wrestle on, for in persistency lies victory, and with the morning may come the wished-for blessing. But not always; there is a struggle with defeat which some of you will have to bear, and it will be well for you in that day to have cultivated a cheerful equanimity. Remember, too, that sometimes "from our desolation only does the better life begin." Even with disaster ahead and ruin imminent, it is better to face them with a smile, and with the head erect, than to crouch at their approach. And, if the fight is for principle and justice, even when failure seems certain, where many have failed before, cling to your ideal, and, like Childe Roland before the dark tower, set the slug-horn to your lips, blow the challenge, and calmly await the conflict.

It has been said that "in patience ye shall win your souls," and what is this patience but an equanimity which enables you to rise superior to the trials of life? Sowing as you shall do beside all waters, I can but wish that you may reap the promised blessing of quietness and of assurance forever, until

Within this life,
Though lifted o'er its strife,

you may, in the growing winters, glean a little of that wisdom which is pure, peaceable, gentle, full of mercy and good fruits, without partiality and without hypocrisy.

The past is always with us, never to be escaped; it alone is enduring; but, amidst the changes and chances which succeed one another so rapidly in this life, we are apt to live too much for the present and too much in the future. On such an occasion as the present, when the *Alma Mater* is in festal array, when we joy in her growing prosperity, it is good to hark back to the olden days and gratefully to recall the men whose labours in the past have made the present possible.

The great possession of any University is its great names. It is not the "pride, pomp and circumstance" of an institution which bring honour, not its wealth, nor the number of its schools, not the students who throng its halls, but the *men* who have trodden in its service the thorny road through toil, even through hate, to the serene abode of Fame, climbing "like stars to their appointed height." These bring glory, and it should thrill the heart of every alumnus of this school, of every teacher in its faculty, as it does mine this day, reverently and thankfully to recall such names amongst its founders as Morgan, Shippen, and Rush, and such men amongst their successors as Wistar, Physick, Barton, and Wood.

Gentlemen of the Faculty—*Noblesse oblige*.

And the sad reality of the past teaches us to-day in the freshness of sorrow at the loss of friends and colleagues, "hid in death's dateless night." We miss from our midst one of your best known instructors, by whose lessons you have profited, and whose example has stimulated many. An earnest teacher, a faithful worker, a loyal son of this University, a good and kindly friend, Edward Bruen has left behind him, amid regrets at a career untimely closed, the memory of a well-spent life.

We mourn to-day, also, with our sister college, the grievous loss which she has sustained in the death of one of her most distinguished teachers, a man who bore with honour an honoured name, and who added lustre to the profession of this city. Such men as Samuel W. Gross can ill be spared. Let us be thankful for the example of a courage which could fight and win; and let us emulate the zeal, energy, and industry which characterized his career.

Personally I mourn the loss of a preceptor, dear to me as a father, the man from whom more than any other I received inspiration, and to whose example and precept I owe the position which enables me to address you to-day. There are those present who will feel it no exaggeration when I say that to have known Palmer Howard[3] was, in the deepest and truest sense of the phrase, a liberal education—

> Whatever way my days decline,
> I felt and feel, tho' left alone,
> His being working in mine own,
> The footsteps of his life in mine.

While preaching to you a doctrine of equanimity, I am, myself, a castaway. Recking not my own rede, I illustrate the inconsistency which so readily besets us. One might have thought that in the premier school of America, in this Civitas Hippocratica, with associations so dear to a lover of his profession, with colleagues so distinguished, and with students so considerate, one might have thought, I say, that the Hercules Pillars of a man's ambition had here been reached. But it has not been so ordained, and to-day I sever my connexion with this University. More than once, gentlemen, in a life rich in the priceless blessings of friends, I have been placed in positions in which no words could express the feelings of my heart, and so it is with me now. The keenest sentiments of gratitude well up from my innermost being at the thought of the kindliness and goodness which have followed me at every step during the past five years. A stranger—I cannot say an alien—among you, I have been made to feel at home—more you could not have done. Could I say more? Whatever the future may have in store of success or of trials, nothing can blot the memory of the happy days I have spent in this city, and nothing can quench the pride I shall always feel at having been associated, even for a time, with a Faculty so notable in the past, so distinguished in the present, as that from which I now part.

Gentlemen, —Farewell, and take with you into the struggle the watchword of the good old Roman—*Aequanimitas.*

---

[1] In 1889, there would have been no female medical students at the University of Pennsylvania, and few elsewhere, although Osler's new institution, Johns Hopkins medical school, would soon accept women—reluctantly, under the influence of fiscal pressures. For further comments, see his remarks in "The Growth of a Profession," pp. 93–94. Osler's own attitude to this question remains equivocal and merits study by some historian or historically oriented physician or student. [C.G.R.]

[2] A reference to the then widespread practice of homeopathy, a school of sectarian medicine that taught, among other things, the efficacy of infinitesimally small doses. [C.G.R.]

[3] His teacher, friend, and dean at McGill. [C.G.R.]

THE FIXED PERIOD*

Osler's "Valedictory Address at Johns Hopkins University" appeared in the Journal of the American Medical Association (vol. 44, pages 705–710, 1905) and again, with the title, "The Fixed Period", in the second edition of Aequanimitas (London, H.K. Lewis; and Philadelphia, P. Blakiston's Sons & Co., 1906).

A S this is the last public function at which I shall appear as a member of the University, I very gladly embrace the opportunity which it offers to express the mingled feelings of gratitude and sorrow which are naturally in my mind—gratitude to you all for sixteen years of exceptionally happy life, sorrow that I am to belong to you no more. Neither stricken deeply in years, nor damaged seriously by illness, you may well wonder at the motives that have induced me to give up a position of such influence and importance, to part from colleagues so congenial, from associates and students so devoted, and to leave a country in which I have so many warm friends, and in which I have been appreciated at so much more than my real worth. It is best that you stay in the wonder-stage. Who can understand another man's motives? Does he always understand his own? This much I may say in explanation—not in palliation. After years of hard work, at the very time when a man's energies begin to flag, and when he feels the need of more leisure, the conditions and surroundings that have made him what he is and that have moulded his character and abilities into something useful in the community—these very circumstances ensure an ever increasing demand upon them; and when the call

* John Hopkins University, Feb. 22, 1905.

of the East comes, which in one form or another is heard by all of us, and which grows louder as we grow older, the call may come like the summons to Elijah, and not alone the plough- ing of the day, but the work of a life, friends, relatives, even father and mother, are left to take up new work in a new field. Or, happier far, if the call comes, as it did to Puran Das in Kipling's story, not to new labours, but to a life "private, un- active, calm, contemplative."

There are several problems in university life suggested by my departure. It may be asked in the first place, whether metab- olism is sufficiently active in the professoriate body, is there change enough? May not the loss of a professor bring stimu- lating benefits to a university? We have not here lost very many—this is not a university that men care to leave—but in looking over its history I do not see that the departure of any one has proved a serious blow. It is strange of how slight value is the unit in a great system. A man may have built up a de- partment and have gained a certain following, local or general; nay, more, he may have had a special value for his mental and moral qualities, and his fission may leave a scar, even an aching scar, but it is not for long. Those of us accustomed to the process know that the organism as a whole feels it about as much as a big polyzoon when a colony breaks off, or a hive of bees after a swarm—'tis not indeed always a calamity, oftentimes it is a relief. Of course upon a few the sense of personal loss falls heavily; in a majority of us the faculty of getting attached to those with whom we work is strongly developed, and some will realize the bitterness of the lines:

> Alas! that all we loved of him should be
> But for our grief as if it had not been.

But to the professor himself these partings belong to the life he has chosen. Like the hero in one of Matthew Arnold's poems, he knows that his heart was not framed to be 'long loved.' Change is the very marrow of his existence—a new set of stu- dents every year, a new set of assistants, a new set of associates every few years to replace those called off to other fields; in any active department there is no constancy, no stability in the human surroundings. And in this there is an element of sadness. A man comes into one's life for a few years, and you become attached to him, interested in his work and in his welfare, and perhaps you grow to love him, as a son, and then off he goes!—leaving you with a bruised heart.

The question may be asked—whether as professors we do not stay too long in one place. It passes my persimmon to tell how some good men—even lovable and righteous men in other respects—have the hardihood to stay in the same position for twenty-five years! To a man of active mind too long attachment to one college is apt to breed self-satisfaction, to narrow his outlook, to foster a local spirit, and to promote senility. Much of the phenomenal success of this institution has been due to the concentration of a group of light-horse intellectuals, without local ties, whose operations were not restricted, whose allegiance indeed was not always national, yet who were willing to serve faithfully in whatever field of action they were placed. And this should be the attitude of a vigilant professoriate. As St. Paul preferred an evangelist without attachments, as more free for the work, so in the general interests of higher education a University President should cherish a proper nomadic spirit in the members of his faculties, even though it be on occasions a seeming detriment. A well-organized College Trust could arrange a rotation of teachers which would be most stimulating all along the line. We are apt to grow stale and thin mentally if kept too long in the same pasture. Transferred to fresh fields, amid new surroundings and other colleagues, a man gets a fillip which may last for several years. Interchange of teachers, national and international, will prove most helpful. How bracing the Turnbull lectures have been, for example. It would be an excellent work for the University Association which met here recently to arrange this interchange of instructors. Even to 'swap' College Presidents now and then might be good for the exchequer. We have an excellent illustration of the value of the plan in the transfer this year from Jena of Prof. Keutgen to give the lectures on History. An international university clearinghouse might be organized to facilitate the work. How delightful it would be to have a return to the mediaeval practice when the professor roamed Europe at his sweet will, or to the halcyon era of the old Greek teachers—of which Empedocles sings:

What days were those Parmenides!
When we were young, when we could number friends
In all the Italian cities like ourselves;
When with elated hearts we joined your train
Ye Sun-born Virgins on the road of truth.

It is more particularly upon the younger men that I would urge the advantages of an early devotion to a peripatetic philosophy of life. Just so soon as you have your second teeth think of a change; get away from the nurse, cut the apron strings of your old teachers, seek new ties in a fresh environment, if possible where you can have a certain measure of freedom and independence. Only do not wait for a fully equipped billet almost as good as that of your master. A small one, poorly appointed, with many students and few opportunities for research, may be just what is needed to bring out the genius—latent and perhaps unrecognized—that will enable you in an unfavourable position to do well what another could not do at all, even in the most helpful surroundings. There are two appalling diseases which only a feline restlessness of mind and body may head off in young men in the academic career. There is a remarkable bodily condition, known as infantilism, in which adolescence does not come at the appointed time, or is deferred until the twentieth year or later, and is then incomplete, so that the childish mind and the childish form and features remain. The mental counterpart is even more common among us. Intellectual infantilism is a well recognized disease, and just as imperfect nutrition may cause failure of the marvellous changes which accompany puberty in the body, so the mind too long fed on the same diet in one place may be rendered rickety or even infantile. Worse than this may happen. A rare, but still more extraordinary, bodily state is that of progeria, in which, as though touched with the wand of some malign fairy, the child does not remain infantile, but skips adolescence, maturity and manhood, and passes at once to senility, looking at eleven or twelve years like a miniature Tithonus "marred and wasted," wrinkled and stunted, a little old man among his toys. It takes great care on the part of any one to live the mental life corresponding to the phases through which his body passes. How few minds reach puberty, how few come to adolescence, how fewer attain maturity! It is really tragic—this wide-spread prevalence of mental infantilism due to careless habits of intellectual feeding. Progeria is an awful malady in a college. Few Faculties escape without an instance or two, and there are certain diets which cause it just as surely as there are waters in some of the Swiss valleys that produce cretinism. I have known an entire faculty attacked. The progeric himself is a nice enough fellow to look at and to play with, but he is sterile, with the mental horizon narrowed, and quite incapable of assimilating the new thoughts of his day and generation.

As in the case of many other diseases, it is more readily prevented than cured, and, taken early, change of air and diet may do much to antagonize a tendency, inherited or acquired. Early stages may be relieved by a prolonged stay at the University Baths of Berlin or Leipzic, or if at the proper time a young man is transferred from an American or Anglican to a Gallic or Teutonic diet. Through no fault of the men, but of the system, due to the unfortunate idea on the part of the denominations that in each one of the States they should have their own educational institutions, collegiate infantilism is far too prevalent, against which the freer air and better diet of the fully equipped State Universities is proving a rapid, as it is the rational, antidote.

Nor would I limit this desire for change to the teachers. The student of the technical school should begin his *wanderjahre* early, not postponing them until he has taken his M.D. or Ph.D. A residence of four years in the one school is apt to breed prejudice and to promote mental astigmatism which the after years may never be able to correct. One great difficulty is the lack of harmony in the curricula of the schools, but this time will correct and, once initiated and encouraged, the better students will take a year, or even two years, in schools other than those at which they intend to graduate.

I am going to be very bold and touch upon another question of some delicacy, but of infinite importance in university life: one that has not been settled in this country. I refer to a fixed period for the teacher, either of time of service or of age. Except in some proprietary schools, I do not know of any institutions in which there is a time limit of, say, twenty years' service, as in some of the London hospitals, or in which a man is engaged for a term of years. Usually the appointment is *ad vitam aut culpam*, as the old phrase reads. It is a very serious matter in our young universities to have all of the professors growing old at the same time. In some places, only an epidemic, a time limit, or an age limit can save the situation. I have two fixed ideas well known to my friends, harmless obsessions with which I sometimes bore them, but which have a direct bearing on this important problem. The first is the comparative uselessness of men above forty years of age. This may seem shocking, and yet read aright the world's history bears out the statement. Take the sum of human achievement in action, in science, in art, in literature—subtract the work of the men above forty, and while we should miss great treasures, even priceless treasures, we would practically be where we are to-day. It is difficult to name a great and far-reaching conquest of the mind which has not been given to the world by a man on whose back the sun was still shining. The effective, moving, vitalizing work of the world is done between the ages of twenty-five and forty—these fifteen golden years of plenty, the anabolic or constructive period, in which there is always a balance in the mental bank and the credit is still good. In the science and art of medicine young or comparatively young men have made every advance of the first rank. Vesalius, Harvey, Hunter, Bichat, Laennec, Virchow, Lister, Koch—the green years were yet upon their heads when their epoch-making studies were made. To modify an old saying, a man is sane morally at thirty, rich mentally at forty, wise spiritually at fifty—or never. The young men should be encouraged and afforded every possible chance to show what is in them. If there is one thing more than another upon which the professors of this university are to be congratulated it is this very sympathy and fellowship with their junior associates, upon whom really in many departments, in mine certainly, has fallen the brunt of the work. And herein lies the chief value of the teacher who has passed his climacteric and is no longer a productive factor, he can play the man midwife as Socrates did to Theaetetus, and determine whether the thoughts which the young men are bringing to the light are false idols or true and noble births.

My second fixed idea is the uselessness of men above sixty years of age, and the incalculable benefit it would be in commercial, political and in professional life if, as a matter of course, men stopped work at this age. In his *Biathanatos* Donne tells us that by the laws of certain wise states sexagenarii were precipitated from a bridge, and in Rome men of that age were not admitted to the suffrage and they were called *Depontani* because the way to the senate was *per pontem*, and they from age were not permitted to come thither. In that charming novel, *The Fixed Period*, Anthony Trollope discusses the practical advantages in modern life of a return to this ancient usage, and the plot hinges upon the admirable scheme of a college into which at sixty men retired for a year of contemplation before a peaceful departure by chloroform.[1] That incalculable benefits might follow such a scheme is apparent to any one who, like myself, is nearing the limit, and who has made a careful study of the calamities which may befall men during the seventh and eighth decades. Still more when he contemplates the many evils which they perpetuate unconsciously, and with impunity. As it can be maintained that all the great advances have come from men under forty, so the history of the world shows that a very large proportion of the evils may be traced to the sexagenarians—nearly all the great mistakes politically and socially, all of the worst poems, most of the bad pictures, a majority of the bad novels, not a few of the bad sermons and speeches. It is not to be denied that occasionally there is a sexagenarian whose mind, as Cicero remarks, stands out of reach of the body's decay. Such a one has learned the secret of Hermippus, that ancient Roman who feeling that the silver cord was loosening cut himself clear from all companions of his own age and betook himself to the company of young men, mingling with their games and studies, and so lived to the age of 153, *puerorum halitu refocillatus et educatus.*[2] And there is truth in the story, since it is only those who live with the young who maintain a fresh outlook on the new problems of the world. The teacher's life should have three periods, study until twenty-five, investigation until forty, profession until sixty, at which age I would have him retired on a double allowance. Whether Anthony Trollope's suggestion of a college and chloroform should be carried out or not I have become a little dubious, as my own time is getting so short. (I may say for the benefit of the public that with a woman I would advise an entirely different plan, since, after sixty her influence on her sex may be most helpful, particularly if aided by those charming accessories, a cap and a fichu.)

II

Such an occasion as the present affords an opportunity to say a few words on the work which the Johns Hopkins foundations have done and may do for medicine. The hospital was organized at a most favourable period, when the profession had at last awakened to its responsibilities, the leading universities had begun to take medical education seriously, and to the public at large had come a glimmering sense of the importance of the scientific investigation of disease and of the advantages of well trained doctors in a community. It would have been an easy matter to have made colossal mistakes with these great organizations. There are instances in which larger bequests have been sterile from the start; but in the history of educational institutions it is hard to name one more prolific than the Johns Hopkins University. Not simply a seed farm, it has been a veritable nursery from which the whole country has been furnished with cuttings, grafts, slips, seedlings, etc. It would be superfluous in this audience to refer to the great work which the Trustees and Mr. Gilman did in twenty-five years—their praise is in all the colleges. But I must pay a tribute to the wise men who planned the hospital, who refused to establish an institution on the old lines—a great city charity for the sick poor, but gave it vital organic connexion with a University. I do not know who was directly responsible for the provision in Mr. Hopkins' will that the hospital should form part of the Medical School, and that it should be an institution for the study as well as for the cure of disease. Perhaps the founder himself may be credited with the idea, but I have always felt that Francis T. King was largely responsible, as he had strong and sensible convictions on the subject, and devoted the last years of his useful life putting them into execution. As first President of the Hospital Board he naturally did much to shape the policy of the institution, and it is a pleasure to recall the zeal and sympathy with which he was always ready to co-operate. It is sad that in so few years all of the members of the original Board have passed away, the last, Mr. Corner—faithful and interested to the end—only a few weeks ago. They did a great work for this city, and their names should be held in everlasting remembrance. Judge Dobbin and James Carey Thomas, in particular, the members of the staff in the early days remember with gratitude for their untiring devotion to the medical school side of the problems which confronted us. To John S. Billings, so long the skilled adviser of the Board, we all turned for advice and counsel, and his influence was deeper and stronger than was always apparent. For the admirable plan of preliminary medical study, and for the shaping of the scientific work before the hospital was opened for patients, we are indebted to Newell Martin, Ira Remsen and W. H. Welch. The present excellent plan of study leading to medicine, in which the classics, science and literature are fully represented, is the outcome of their labours.

About this time sixteen years ago Mr. King, Dr. Billings, Dr. Welch and myself had many conferences with reference to the opening of the hospital. I had been appointed January 1st, but had not yet left Philadelphia. As so often happens the last steps in a great organization are the most troublesome, and after some delay the whole matter was intrusted to Mr. Gilman, who became acting director, and in a few months everything was ready, and on May 7 the hospital was opened. I look back with peculiar pleasure to my association with Mr. Gilman. It was both an education and a revelation. I had never before been brought into close contact with a man who loved difficulties just for the pleasure of making them disappear. But I am not going to speak of those happy days lest it should forestall the story I have written of the inner history of the first period of the hospital.

At the date of the organization of the hospital the two great problems before the profession of this country were, how to give to students a proper education, in other words how to give them the culture, the science and the art commensurate with the dignity of a learned profession; and, secondly, how to make this great and rich country a contributor to the science of medicine.

The conditions under which the medical school opened in 1893 were unique in the history of American medicine. It would have been an easy matter, following the lead of the better schools, to have an entrance examination which guaranteed that a man had an ordinary education, but Miss Garett's splendid gift enabled us to say, no! we do not want a large number of half-educated students; we prefer a select group trained in the sciences preliminary to medicine, and in the languages which will be most useful for a modern physician. It was an experiment, and we did not expect more than twenty five or thirty students each year for eight or ten years at least. As is so often the case, the country was better prepared than we thought to meet our conditions, and the number of admissions to the school has risen until we have about reached our capacity. Our example in demanding the preliminary arts or science course for admission to the school has been followed by Harvard, and is to be adopted at Columbia. It is not a necessary measure in all the schools, but there has been everywhere a very salutary increase in the stringency of the entrance examinations. Before we took up the work great reforms in the scientific teaching in medicine had already begun in this country. Everywhere laboratory work had replaced to some extent the lecture, and practical courses in physiology, pathology and pharmacology had been organized. We must not forget however that to Newell Martin, the first professor of physiology in this university, is due the introduction of practical classes in biology and physiology. The rapid growth of the school necessitated the erection of a separate building for physiology, pharmacology and physiological chemistry, and in these departments and in anatomy the equipment is as complete as is required. Of the needs in pathology, hygiene and experimental pathology this is not the occasion to speak. It is sufficient to say that for instruction in the sciences, upon which the practice of the art is based, the school is in first class condition.

Indeed the rapidity with which the scientific instruction in our medical schools has been brought to a high level is one of the most remarkable educational features of the past twenty years. Even in small unendowed colleges admirable courses are given in bacteriology and pathology, and sometimes in the more difficult subject of practical physiology. But the demand and the necessity for these special courses has taxed to the utmost the resources of the private schools. The expense of the new method of teaching is so great that the entire class fees are absorbed by the laboratories. The consequence is that the old proprietary colleges are no longer profitable ventures, certainly not in the north, and fortunately they are being forced into closer affiliation with the universities, as it is not an easy matter to get proper endowments for private corporations.

The great difficulty is in the third part of the education of the student: viz., his art. In the old days when a lad was apprenticed to a general practitioner, he had good opportunities to pick up the essentials of a rough and ready art, and the system produced many self-reliant, resourceful men. Then with the multiplication of the medical schools and increasing rivalry between them came the two year course, which for half a century lay like a blight on the medical profession, retarding its progress, filling its ranks with half-educated men, and pandering directly to all sorts of quackery, humbuggery and fraud among the public. The awakening came about thirty years ago, and now there is scarcely a school in the country which has not a four years course, and all are trying to get clear of the old shackles and teach rational medicine in a rational way. But there are extraordinary difficulties in teaching the medical student his Art. It is not hard, for example, to teach him all about the disease pneumonia, how it prevails in the winter and spring, how fatal it always has been, all about the germ, all about the change which the disease causes in the lungs and in the heart—he may become learned, deeply learned, on the subject—but put him beside a case, and he may not know which lung is involved, and he does not know how to find out, and if he did find out, he might be in doubt whether to put an ice-bag or a poultice on the affected side, whether to bleed or to give opium, whether to give a dose of medicine every hour or none at all, and he may not have the faintest notion whether the signs look ominous or favourable. So also with other aspects of the art of the general practitioner. A student may know all about the bones of the wrist, in fact he may carry a set in his pocket and know every facet and knob and nodule on them, he may have dissected a score of arms, and yet when he is called to see Mrs. Jones who has fallen on the ice and broken her wrist, he may not know a Colles' from a Pott's fracture, and as for setting it *secundum artem*, he may not have the faintest notion, never having seen a case. Or he may be called to preside at one of those awful domestic tragedies—the sudden emergency, some terrible accident of birth or of childhood, that requires skill, technical skill, courage—the courage of full knowledge, and if he has not been in the obstetrical wards, if he has not been trained practically, if he has not had the opportunities that are the rights of every medical student, he may fail at the critical moment, a life, two lives, may be lost, sacrificed to ignorance, often to helpless, involuntary ignorance. By far the greatest work of the

Johns Hopkins Hospital has been the demonstration to the profession of the United States and to the public of this country of how medical students should be instructed in their art. I place it first because it was the most needed lesson, I place it first because it has done the most good as a stimulating example, and I place it first because never before in the history of this country have medical students lived and worked in a hospital as part of its machinery, as an essential part of the work of the wards. In saying this, Heaven forbid that I should obliquely disparage the good and faithful work of my colleagues elsewhere. But the amphitheatre clinic, the ward and dispensary classes, are but bastard substitutes for a system which makes the medical student himself help in the work of the hospital as part of its human machinery. He does not see the pneumonia case in the amphitheatre from the benches, but he follows it day by day, hour by hour; he has his time so arranged that he can follow it; he sees and studies similar cases and the disease itself becomes his chief teacher, and he knows its phases and variations as depicted in the living; he learns under skilled direction when to act and when to refrain, he learns insensibly principles of practice and he possibly escapes a "nickel-in-the-slot" attitude of mind which has been the curse of the physician in the treatment of disease. And the same with the other branches of his art; he gets a first hand knowledge which, if he has any sense, may make him wise unto the salvation of his fellows. And all this has come about through the wise provision that the hospital was to be part of the medical school, and it has become for the senior students, as it should be, their college. Moreover they are not in it upon sufferance and admitted through side-doors, but they are welcomed as important aids without which the work could not be done efficiently. The whole question of the practical education of the medical student is one in which the public is vitally interested. Sane, intelligent physicians and surgeons with culture, science, and art, are worth much in a community, and they are worth paying for in rich endowments of our medical schools and hospitals. Personally, there is nothing in life in which I take greater pride than in my connexion with the organization of the medical clinic of the Johns Hopkins Hospital and with the introduction of the old-fashioned methods of practical instruction. I desire no other epitaph—no hurry about it, I may say—than the statement that I taught medical students in the wards, as I regard this as by far the most useful and important work I have been called upon to do.

The second great problem is a much more difficult one, surrounded as it is with obstacles inextricably connected with the growth and expansion of a comparatively new country. For years the United States had been the largest borrower in the scientific market of the world, and more particularly in the sciences relating to medicine. To get the best that the world offered, our young men had to go abroad; only here and there was a laboratory of physiology or pathology, and then equipped as a rule for teaching. The change in twenty years has been remarkable. There is scarcely to-day a department of scientific medicine which is not represented in our larger cities by men who are working as investigators, and American scientific medicine is taking its rightful place in the world's work. Nothing shows this more plainly than the establishment within a few years of journals devoted to scientific subjects; and the active participation of this school as a leader is well illustrated by the important publications which have been started by its members. The Hospital Trustees early appreciated the value of these scientific publications, and the Bulletin and the Reports have done much to spread the reputation of the Hospital as a medical centre throughout the world. But let us understand clearly that only a beginning has been made. For one worker in pathology— a man, I mean, who is devoting his life to the study of the causes of diseases—there are twenty-five at least in Germany, and for one in this country there are a dozen laboratories of the first class in any one of the more important sciences cognate to medicine. It is not alone that the money is lacking; the men are not always at hand. When the right man is available he quickly puts American science into the forefront. Let me give you an illustration. Anatomy is a fundamental branch in medicine. There is no school, even amid sylvan glades, without its dissecting room; but it has been a great difficulty to get the higher anatomy represented in American universities. Plenty of men have always been available to teach the subject to medical students, but when it came to questions of morphology and embryology and the really scientific study of the innumerable problems connected with them, it was only here and there and not in a thorough manner that the subjects were approached. And the young men had to go abroad to see a completely equipped, modern working anatomical institute. There is to-day connected with this university a school of anatomy of which any land might be proud, and the work of Dr. Mall demonstrates what can be done when the man fits his environment.

It is a hopeful sign to see special schools established for the study of disease such as the Rockefeller Institute in New York, the McCormick Institute in Chicago and the Phipps Institute in Philadelphia. They will give a great impetus in the higher lines of work in which the country has heretofore been so weak. But it makes one green with envy to see how much our German brethren are able to do. Take, for example, the saddest chapter in the history of disease—insanity, the greatest curse of civilized life. Much has been done in the United States for the care of the insane, much in places for the study of the disease, and I may say that the good work which has been inaugurated in this line at the Sheppard Hospital is attracting attention everywhere; but what a bagatelle it seems in comparison with the modern development of the subject in Germany, with its great psychopathic clinics connected with each university, where early and doubtful cases are skilfully studied and skilfully treated. The new department for insanity connected with the University of Munich has cost nearly half a million dollars! Of the four new departments for which one side of the hospital grounds lies vacant, and which will be built within the next twenty-five years, one should be a model psychopathic clinic to which the acute and curable cases may be sent. The second, a clinic for the diseases of children. Much has been done with our out-patient department under Dr. Booker, who has helped to clarify one of the dark problems in infant mortality, but we need a building with fine wards and laboratories in which may be done work of a character as notable and worldwide as that done in Dr. Kelly's division for the diseases of women.* The third great department for which a separate building must be provided is that of Syphilis and Dermatology. Already no small share of the reputation of this hospital has come from the good work in these specialties by the late Dr. Brown, by Dr. Gilchrist, and by Dr. Hugh Young; and lastly, for diseases of the eye, ear, and throat, a large separate clinic is needed, which will give to these all-important subjects the equipment they deserve.

For how much to be thankful have we who have shared in the initiation of the work of these two great institutions. We have been blessed with two remarkable Presidents, whose active sympathies have been a stimulus in every department, and whose good sense has minimized the loss of energy through friction between the various parts of the machine—a loss from which colleges are very prone to suffer. A noteworthy feature is that in so motley a collection from all parts of the country the men should have fitted into each other's lives so smoothly and peacefully, so that the good fellowship and harmony in the faculties has been delightful. And we have been singularly blessed in our relationship with the citizens, who have not only learned to appreciate the enormous benefits which these great trusts confer upon the city and the state, but they have come forward in a noble way to make possible a new era in the life of the university. And we of the medical faculty have to feel very grateful to the profession, to whose influence and support much of the success of the hospital and the medical school is due; and not only to the physicians of the city and of the state, who have dealt so truly with us, but to the profession of the entire country, and more particularly to that of the Southern States, whose confidence we have enjoyed in such a practical way. Upon a maintenance of this confidence the future rests.

---

* It is most gratifying to know that the Harriet Lane Johnston Hospital for children will be associated with the Johns Hopkins Hospital, and will meet the requirements of which I have spoken.

The character of the work of the past sixteen years is the best guarantee of its permanence.

What has been accomplished is only an earnest of what shall be done in the future. Upon our heels a fresh perfection must tread, born of us, fated to excel us. We have but served and have but seen a beginning. Personally I feel deeply grateful to have been permitted to join in this noble work and to have been united in it with men of such high and human ideals.

---

[1] From this innocent reference arose a misunderstanding of classic dimensions. Fanned by headline-seeking newspapers, a few critics accused Osler of openly advocating the chloroforming of our elder citizens, a posture so foreign to Osler's true temperament that it should have been obviously false. For a description of this incident see C.G. Roland, "The Infamous William Osler," JAMA 193: 436–438, 1965. [C.G.R.]

[2] 'revived and nurtured by the inspiration of boys' [C.G.R.]

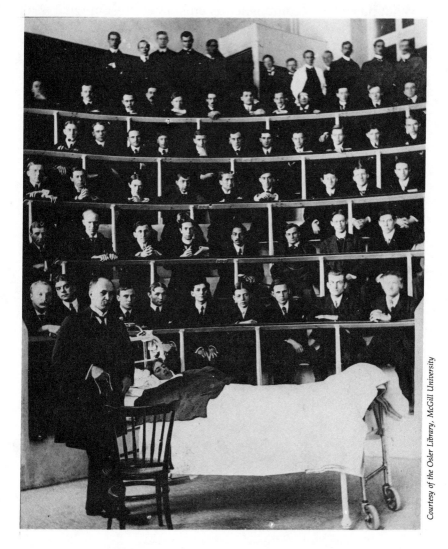

Osler with students at Johns Hopkins

THE STUDENT LIFE*

"The Student Life. A Farewell Address to Canadian and American Medical Students," was published in several locations in 1905, including the Canada Lancet *(vol. 39, pages 121–138, 1905–06).* It was reprinted in Aequanimitas *(2nd edition, 1906)* and in Christopher Morley's Modern Essays *(New York, Harcourt, Horace & Co., 1921).*

EXCEPT it be a lover, no one is more interesting as an object of study than a student. Shakespeare might have made him a fourth in his immortal group. The lunatic with his fixed idea, the poet with his fine frenzy, the lover with his frantic idolatry, and the student aflame with the desire for knowledge are of "imagination all compact." To an absorbing passion, a whole-souled devotion, must be joined an enduring energy, if the student is to become a devotee of the grey-eyed goddess to whose law his services are bound. Like the quest of the Holy Grail, the quest of Minerva is not for all. For the one, the pure life; for the other, what Milton calls "a strong propensity of nature." Here again the student often resembles the poet—he is born, not made. While the resultant of two moulding forces, the accidental, external conditions, and the hidden germinal energies, which produce in each one of us national, family, and individual traits, the true student possesses in some measure a divine spark which sets at naught their laws. Like the Snark, he defies definition, but there are three unmistakable signs by which you may recognize the genuine article from a Boojum—an absorbing desire to know the truth, an unswerving stead-

* A farewell address to American and Canadian medical students, 1905.

fastness in its pursuit, and an open, honest heart, free from suspicion, guile, and jealousy.

At the outset do not be worried about this big question— Truth. It is a very simple matter if each one of you starts with the desire to get as much as possible. No human being is constituted to know the truth, the whole truth, and nothing but the truth; and even the best of men must be content with fragments, with partial glimpses, never the full fruition. In this unsatisfied quest the attitude of mind, the desire, the thirst— a thirst that from the soul must rise!—the fervent longing, are the be-all and the end-all. What is the student but a lover courting a fickle mistress who ever eludes his grasp? In this very elusiveness is brought out his second great characteristic— steadfastness of purpose. Unless from the start the limitations incident to our frail human faculties are frankly accepted, nothing but disappointment awaits you. The truth is the best you can get with your best endeavour, the best that the best men accept—with this you must learn to be satisfied, retaining at the same time with due humility an earnest desire for an ever larger portion. Only by keeping the mind plastic and receptive does the student escape perdition. It is not, as Charles Lamb remarks, that some people do not know what to do with truth when it is offered to them, but the tragic fate is to reach, after years of patient search, a condition of mind-blindness in which the truth is not recognized, though it stares you in the face. This can never happen to a man who has followed step by step the growth of a truth, and who knows the painful phases of its evolution. It is one of the great tragedies of life that every truth has to struggle to acceptance against honest but mind-blind students. Harvey knew his contemporaries well, and for twelve successive years demonstrated the circulation of the blood before daring to publish the facts on which the truth was based.* Only steadfastness of purpose and humility enable the student to shift his position to meet the new conditions in which new truths are born, or old ones modified beyond recognition.

* "These views, as usual, pleased some more, others less; some chid and calumniated me, and laid it to me as a crime that I had dared to depart from the precepts and opinions of all Anatomists."—*De Motu Cordis*, chap. 1.

And, thirdly, the honest heart will keep him in touch with his fellow students, and furnish that sense of comradeship without which he travels an arid waste alone. I say advisedly an honest *heart*—the honest head is prone to be cold and stern, given to judgment, not mercy, and not always able to entertain that true charity which, while it thinketh no evil, is anxious to put the best possible interpretation upon the motives of a fellow worker. It will foster, too, an attitude of generous, friendly rivalry untinged by the green peril, jealousy, that is the best preventive of the growth of a bastard scientific spirit, loving seclusion and working in a lock-and-key laboratory, as timorous of light as is a thief.

You have all become brothers in a great society, not apprentices, since that implies a master, and nothing should be further from the attitude of the teacher than much that is meant in that word, used though it be in another sense, particularly by our French brethren in a most delightful way, signifying a bond of intellectual filiation. A fraternal attitude is not easy to cultivate—the chasm between the chair and the bench is difficult to bridge. Two things have helped to put up a cantilever across the gulf. The successful teacher is no longer on a height, pumping knowledge at high pressure into passive receptacles. The new methods have changed all this. He is no longer *Sir Oracle*, perhaps unconsciously by his very manner antagonizing minds to whose level he cannot possibly descend, but he is a senior student anxious to help his juniors. When a simple, earnest spirit animates a college, there is no appreciable interval between the teacher and the taught—both are in the same class, the one a little more advanced than the other. So animated, the student feels that he has joined a family whose honour is his honour, whose welfare is his own, and whose interests should be his first consideration.

The hardest conviction to get into the mind of a beginner is that the education upon which he is engaged is not a college course, not a medical course, but a life course, for which the work of a few years under teachers is but a preparation. Whether you will falter and fail in the race or whether you will be faithful to the end depends on the training before the start, and on your staying powers, points upon which I need not enlarge. You can all become good students, a few may become great students, and now and again one of you will be found who does easily and well what others cannot do at all, or very badly, which is John Ferriar's excellent definition of a genius.

In the hurry and bustle of a business world, which is the life of this continent, it is not easy to train first-class students. Under present conditions it is hard to get the needful seclusion, on which account it is that our educational market is so full of wayside fruit. I have always been much impressed by the advice of St. Chrysostom: "Depart from the highway and transplant thyself in some enclosed ground, for it is hard for a tree which stands by the wayside to keep her fruit till it be ripe." The dilettante is abroad in the land, the man who is always venturing on tasks for which he is imperfectly equipped, a habit of mind fostered by the multiplicity of subjects of the curriculum; and while many things are studied, few are studied thoroughly. Men will not take time to get to the heart of a matter. After all, concentration is the price the modern student pays for success. Thoroughness is the most difficult habit to acquire, but it is the pearl of great price, worth all the worry and trouble of the search. The dilettante lives an easy, butterfly life, knowing nothing of the toil and labour with which the treasures of knowledge are dug out of the past, or wrung by patient research in the laboratories. Take, for example, the early history of this country—how easy for the student of the one type to get a smattering, even a fairly full acquaintance with the events of the French and Spanish settlements. Put an original document before him, and it might as well be Arabic. What we need is the other type, the man who knows the records, who, with a broad outlook and drilled in what may be called the embryology of history, has yet a powerful vision for the minutiae of life. It is these kitchen and backstair men who are to be encouraged, the men who know the subject in hand in all possible relationships. Concentration has its drawbacks. It is possible to become so absorbed in the problem of the "enclitic δξ," or the structure of the flagella of the Trichomonas, or of the toes of the prehistoric horse, that the student loses the sense of proportion in his work, and even wastes a lifetime in researches which are valueless because not in touch with current knowledge. You remember poor Casaubon, in *Middlemarch*, whose painful scholarship was lost on this account. The best preventive to this is to get denationalized early. The true student is a citizen of the world, the allegiance of whose soul, at any rate, is too precious to be restricted to a single country. The great minds, the great works transcend all limitations of time, of language, and of race, and the scholar can never feel initiated into the company of the elect until he can approach all of life's problems from the cosmopolitan standpoint. I care not in what subject he may work, the full knowledge cannot be reached without drawing on supplies from lands other than his own—French, English, German, American, Japanese, Russian, Italian—there must be no discrimination by the loyal student, who should willingly draw from any and every source with an open mind and a stern resolve to render unto all their dues. I care not on what stream of knowledge he may embark, follow up its course, and the rivulets that feed it flow from many lands. If the work is to be effective he must keep in touch with scholars in other countries. How often has it happened that years of precious time have been given to a problem already solved or shown to be insoluble, because of the ignorance of what had been done elsewhere. And it is not only book knowledge and journal knowledge, but a knowledge of men that is needed. The student will, if possible, see the men in other lands. Travel not only widens the vision and gives certainties in place of vague surmises, but the personal contact with foreign workers enables him to appreciate better the failings or successes in his own line of work, perhaps to look with more charitable eyes on the work of some brother whose limitations and opportunities have been more restricted than his own. Or, in contact with a mastermind, he may take fire, and the glow of the enthusiasm may be the inspiration of his life. Concentration must then be associated with large views on the relation of the problem, and a knowledge of its status elsewhere; otherwise it may land him in the slough of a specialism so narrow that is has depth and no breadth, or he may be led to make what he believes to be important discoveries, but which have long been current coin in other lands. It is sad to think that the day of the great polymathic student is at an end; that we may, perhaps, never again see a Scaliger, a Haller, or a Humboldt—men who took the whole field of knowledge for their domain and viewed it as from a pinnacle. And yet a great specializing generalist may arise, who can tell? Some twentieth-century Aristotle may be now tugging at his bottle, as little dreaming as are his parents or his friends of a conquest of the mind, beside which the wonderful victories of the Stagirite will look pale. The value of a really great student to the country is equal to half a dozen grain elevators or a new transcontinental railway. He is a commodity singularly fickle and variable, and not to be grown to order. So far as his advent is concerned there is no telling when or where he may arise. The conditions seem to be present even under the most unlikely externals. Some of the greatest students this country has produced have come from small villages and country places. It is impossible to predict from a study of the environment, which a "strong propensity of nature," to quote Milton's phrase again, will easily bend or break.

The student must be allowed full freedom in his work, undisturbed by the utilitarian spirit of the Philistine, who cries, *Cui bono?* and distrusts pure science. The present remarkable position in applied science and in industrial trades of all sorts has been made possible by men who did pioneer work in chemistry, in physics, in biology, and in physiology, without a thought in their researches of any practical application. The members of this higher group of productive students are rarely understood by the common spirits, who appreciate as little their unselfish devotion as their unworldly neglect of the practical side of the problems.

Everywhere now the medical student is welcomed as an honoured member of the guild. There was a time, I confess, and it is within memory of some of us, when, like Falstaff, he was given to "taverns and sack and wine and metheglins, and to drinkings and swearings and starings, pribbles and prabbles"; but all that has changed with the curriculum, and the "Meds" now roar you as gently as the "Theologs." On account of the peculiar character of the subject-matter of your studies, what I have said upon the general life and mental attitude of the student applies with tenfold force to you. Man, with all his mental and bodily anomalies and diseases—the machine in order, the machine in disorder, and the business yours to put it to rights. Through all the phases of its career this most complicated mechanism of this wonderful world will be the subject of our study and of your care—the naked, new-born infant, the artless child, the lad and the lassie just aware of the tree of knowledge overhead, the strong man in the pride of life, the woman with the benediction of maternity on her brow, and the aged, peaceful in the contemplation of the past. Almost everything has been renewed in the science and in the art of medicine, but all through the long centuries there has been no variableness or shadow of change in the essential features of the life which is our contemplation and our care. The sick love-child of Israel's sweet singer, the plague-stricken hopes of the great Athenian statesman, Elpenor bereft of his beloved Artemidora, and "Tully's daughter mourned so tenderly," are not of any age or any race—they are here with us to-day, with the Hamlets, the Ophelias, and the Lears. Amid an eternal heritage of sorrow and suffering our work is laid, and this eternal note of sadness would be insupportable if the daily tragedies were not relieved by the spectacle of the heroism and devotion displayed by the actors. Nothing will sustain you more potently than the power to recognize in your humdrum routine, as perhaps it may be thought, the true poetry of life—the poetry of the commonplace, of the ordinary man, of the plain, toil-worn woman, with their loves and their joys, their sorrows and their griefs. The comedy, too, of life will be spread before you, and nobody laughs more often than the doctor at the pranks Puck plays upon the Titanias and the Bottoms among his patients. The humorous side is really almost as frequently turned towards him as the tragic. Lift up one hand to heaven and thank your stars if they have given you the proper sense to enable you to appreciate the inconceivably droll situations in which we catch our fellow creatures. Unhappily, this is one of the free gifts of the gods, unevenly distributed, not bestowed on all, or on all in equal portions.

In undue measure it is not without risk, and in any case in the doctor is is better appreciated by the eye than expressed on the tongue. Hilarity and good humour, a breezy cheerfulness, a nature "sloping toward the southern side," as Lowell has it, help enormously both in the study and in the practice of medicine. To many of a sombre and sour disposition it is hard to maintain good spirits amid the trials and tribulations of the day, and yet it is an unpardonable mistake to go about among patients with a long face.

Divide your attentions equally between books and men. The strength of the student of books is to sit still—two or three hours at a stretch—eating the heart out of a subject with pencil and notebook in hand, determined to master the details and intricacies, focussing all your energies on its difficulties. Get accustomed to test all sorts of book problems and statements for yourself, and take as little as possible on trust. The Hunterian "Do not think, but try" attitude of mind is the important one to cultivate. The question came up one day, when discussing the grooves left on the nails after fever, how long it took for the nail to grow out, from root to edge. A majority of the class had no further interest; a few looked it up in books; two men marked their nails at the root with nitrate of silver, and a few months later had positive knowledge on the subject. They showed the proper spirit. The little points that come up in your reading try to test for yourselves. With one fundamental difficulty many of you will have to contend from the outset—a lack of proper preparation for really hard study. No one can have watched successive groups of young men pass through the special schools without profoundly regretting the haphazard, fragmentary character of their preliminary education. It does seem too bad that we cannot have a student in his eighteenth year sufficiently grounded in the humanities and in the sciences preliminary to medicine- -but this is an educational problem upon which only a Milton or a Locke could discourse with profit. With pertinacity you can overcome the preliminary defects and once thoroughly interested, the work in books becomes a pastime. A serious drawback in the student life is the selfconsciousness, bred of too close devotion to books. A man gets shy, "dysopic," as old

Timothy Bright calls it, and shuns the looks of men, and blushes like a girl.

The strength of a student of men is to travel—to study men, their habits, character, mode of life, their behaviour under varied conditions, their vices, virtues, and peculiarities. Begin with a careful observation of your fellow students and of your teachers; then, every patient you see is a lesson in much more than the malady from which he suffers. Mix as much as you possibly can with the outside world, and learn its ways. Cultivated systematically, the student societies, the students' union, the gymnasium, and the outside social circle will enable you to conquer the diffidence so apt to go with bookishness and which may prove a very serious drawback in after-life. I cannot too strongly impress upon the earnest and attentive men among you the necessity of overcoming this unfortunate failing in your student days. It is not easy for every one to reach a happy medium, and the distinction between a proper self-confidence and "cheek," particularly in junior students, is not always to be made. The latter is met with chiefly among the student pilgrims who, in travelling down the Delectable Mountains, have gone astray and have passed to the left hand, where lieth the country of Conceit, the country in which you remember the brisk lad Ignorance met Christian.

I wish we could encourage on this continent among our best students the habit of wandering. I do not know that we are quite prepared for it, as there is still great diversity in the curricula, even among the leading schools, but it is undoubtedly a great advantage to study under different teachers, as the mental horizon is widened and the sympathies enlarged. The practice would do much to lessen that narrow "I am of Paul and I am of Apollos" spirit which is hostile to the best interests of the profession.

There is much that I would like to say on the question of work, but I can spare only a few moments for a word or two. Who will venture to settle upon so simple a matter as the best time for work? One will tell us there is no best time; all are equally good; and truly, all times are the same to a man whose soul is absorbed in some great problem. The other day I asked

Edward Martin, the well-known story-writer, what time he found best for work. "Not in the evening, and never between meals!" was his answer, which may appeal to some of my hearers. One works best at night; another, in the morning; a majority of the students of the past favour the latter. Erasmus, the great exemplar, says, "Never work at night; it dulls the brain and hurts the health." One day, going with George Ross through Bedlam, Dr. Savage, at that time the physician in charge, remarked upon two great groups of patients—those who were depressed in the morning and those who were cheerful, and he suggested that the spirits rose and fell with the bodily temperature—those with very low morning temperatures were depressed, and vice versa. This, I believe, expresses a truth which may explain the extraordinary difference in the habits of students in this matter of the time at which the best work can be done. Outside of the asylum there are also the two great types, the student-lark who loves to see the sun rise, who comes to breakfast with a cheerful morning face, never so "fit" as at 6 a.m. We all know the type. What a contrast to the student-owl with his saturnine morning face, thoroughly unhappy, cheated by the wretched breakfast bell of the two best hours of the day for sleep, no appetite, and permeated with an unspeakable hostility to his *vis-à-vis*, whose morning garrulity and good humour are equally offensive. Only gradually, as the day wears on and his temperature rises, does he become endurable to himself and to others. But see him really awake at 10 p.m. while our blithe lark is in hopeless coma over his books, from which it is hard to rouse him sufficiently to get his boots off for bed, our lean owl-friend, Saturn no longer in the ascendant, with bright eyes and cheery face, is ready for four hours of anything you wish—deep study, or

Heart-affluence in discursive talk,

and by 2 a.m. he will undertake to unsphere the spirit of Plato. In neither a virtue, in neither a fault we must recognize these two types of students, differently constituted, owing possibly—

though I have but little evidence for the belief—to thermal peculiarities.

II

In the days of probation the student's life may be lived by
each one of you in its fullness and in its joys, but the difficulties
arise in the break which follows departure from college and the
entrance upon new duties. Much will now depend on the
attitude of mind which has been encouraged. If the work has
been for your degree, if the diploma has been its sole aim and
object, you will rejoice in a freedom from exacting and possibly
unpleasant studies, and with your books you will throw away
all thoughts of further systematic work. On the other hand,
with good habits of observation you may have got deep enough
into the subject to feel that there is still much to be learned,
and if you have had ground into you the lesson that the collegiate period is only the beginning of the student life, there
is a hope that you may enter upon the useful career of the
student-practitioner. Five years, at least, of trial await the man
after parting from his teachers, and entering upon an independent course—years upon which his future depends, and
from which his horoscope may be cast with certainty. It is all
the same whether he settles in a country village or goes on with
hospital and laboratory work; whether he takes a prolonged
trip abroad; or whether he settles down in practice with a father
or a friend—these five waiting years fix his fate so far as the
student life is concerned. Without any strong natural propensity
to study, he may feel such a relief after graduation that the
effort to take to books is beyond his mental strength, and a
weekly journal with an occasional textbook furnish pabulum
enough, at least to keep his mind hibernating. But ten years
later he is dead mentally, past any possible hope of galvanizing
into life as a student, fit to do a routine practice, often a capable,
resourceful man, but without any deep convictions, and probably more interested in stocks or in horses than in diagnosis

or therapeutics. But this is not always the fate of the student who finishes his work on Commencement Day. There are men full of zeal in practice who give good service to their fellow creatures, who have not the capacity or the energy to keep up with the times. While they have lost interest in science, they are loyal members of the profession, and appreciate their responsibilities as such. That fateful first lustrum ruins some of our most likely material. Nothing is more trying to the soldier than inaction, to mark time while the battle is raging all about him; and waiting for practice is a serious strain under which many yield. In the cities it is not so hard to keep up: there is work in the dispensaries and colleges, and the stimulus of the medical societies; but in smaller towns and in the country it takes a strong man to live through the years of waiting without some deterioration. I wish the custom of taking junior men as partners and assistants would grow on this continent. It has become a necessity, and no man in large general practice can do his work efficiently without skilled help. How incalculably better for the seniors, how beneficial to the patients, how helpful in every way if each one of you, for the first five or ten years, was associated with an older practitioner, doing his night work, his laboratory work, his chores of all sorts. You would, in this way, escape the chilling and killing isolation of the early years, and amid congenial surroundings you could, in time, develop into that flower of our calling—the cultivated general practitioner. May this be the destiny of a large majority of you! Have no higher ambition! You cannot reach any better position in a community; the family doctor is the man behind the gun, who does our effective work. That his life is hard and exacting; that he is underpaid and overworked; that he has but little time for study and less for recreation—these are the blows that may give finer temper to his steel, and bring out the nobler elements in his character. What lot or portion has the general practitioner in the student life? Not, perhaps, the fruitful heritage of Judah or Benjamin but he may make of it the goodly portion of Ephraim. A man with powers of observation, well trained in the wards, and with the strong natural propensity to which I have so often referred, may live the ideal student life, and even reach the higher levels of scholarship. Adams, of Banchory (a little Aberdeenshire village), was not only a good practitioner and a skilful operator, but he was an excellent naturalist. This is by no means an unusual or remarkable combination, but Adams became, in addition, one of the great scholars of the profession. He had a perfect passion for the classics, and amid a very exacting practice found time to read "almost every Greek work which has come down to us from antiquity, except the ecclesiastical writers." He translated the works of Paulus Aegineta, the works of Hippocrates, and the works of Aretaeus, all of which are in the Sydenham Society's publications, monuments of the patient skill and erudition of a Scottish village doctor, an incentive to every one of us to make better use of our precious time.

Given the sacred hunger and proper preliminary training, the student-practitioner requires at least three things with which to stimulate and maintain his education, a notebook, a library, and a quinquennial braindusting. I wish I had time to speak of the value of note-taking. You can do nothing as a student in practice without it. Carry a small notebook which will fit into your waistcoat pocket, and never ask a new patient a question without notebook and pencil in hand. After the examination of a pneumonia case two minutes will suffice to record the essentials in the daily progress. Routine and system when once made a habit, facilitate work, and the busier you are the more time you will have to make observations after examining a patient. Jot a comment at the end of the notes: "clear case," "case illustrating obscurity of symptoms," "error in diagnosis," etc. The making of observations, may become the exercise of a jackdaw trick, like the craze which so many of us have to collect articles of all sorts. The study of the cases, the relation they bear to each other and to the cases in literature—here comes in the difficulty. Begin early to make a threefold category—clear cases, doubtful cases, mistakes. And learn to play the game fair, no self-deception, no shrinking from the truth; mercy and consideration for the other man, but none for yourself, upon whom you have to keep an incessant watch. You remember Lincoln's famous *mot* about the impossibility of fooling all of the people all the time. It does not hold good for the individual who can fool himself to his heart's content all of the time. If necessary, be cruel; use the knife and the cautery to cure the intumescence and moral necrosis which you will feel in the posterior parietal region, in Gall and Spurzheim's centre of self-esteem, where you will find a sore spot after you have made a mistake in diagnosis. It is only by getting your cases grouped in this way that you can make any real progress in your post-collegiate education; only in this way can you gain wisdom with experience. It is a common error to think that the more a doctor sees the greater his experience and the more he knows. No one ever drew a more skilful distinction than Cowper in his oft-quoted lines, which I am never tired of repeating in a medical audience:

> Knowledge and wisdom, far from being one,
> Have oft-times no connexion. Knowledge dwells
> In heads replete with thoughts of other men;
> Wisdom in minds attentive to their own.
> Knowledge is proud that he has learned so much;
> Wisdom is humble that he knows no more.

What we call sense or wisdom is knowledge, ready for use, made effective, and bears the same relation to knowledge itself that bread does to wheat. The full knowledge of the parts of a steam engine and the theory of its action may be possessed by a man who could not be trusted to pull the lever to its throttle. It is only by collecting data and using them that you can get sense. One of the most delightful sayings of antiquity is the remark of Heraclitus upon his predecessors—that they had much knowledge but no sense—which indicates that the noble old Ephesian had a keen appreciation of their difference; and the distinction, too, is well drawn by Tennyson in the oft-quoted line:

> Knowledge comes but wisdom lingers.

Of the three well-stocked rooms which it should be the ambition of every young doctor to have in his house, the library, the laboratory, and the nursery—books, balances, and bairns— as he may not achieve all three, I would urge him to start at any rate with the books and the balances. A good weekly and a good monthly journal to begin with, and read them. Then, for a systematic course of study, supplement your college text- books with the larger systems—Allbutt or Nothnagel—a system of surgery, and, as your practice increases, make a habit of buying a few special monographs every year. Read with two objects: first, to acquaint yourself with the current knowledge on the subject and the steps by which it has been reached; and secondly, and more important, read to understand and analyse your cases. To this line of work we should direct the attention of the student before he leaves the medical school, pointing in specific cases just where the best articles are to be found, send- ing him to the Index Catalogue—that marvellous storehouse, every page of which is interesting and the very titles instructive. Early learn to appreciate the differences between the descrip- tions of disease and the manifestations of that disease in an individual—the difference between the composite portrait and one of the component pictures. By exercise of a little judgment you can collect at moderate cost a good working library. Try, in the waiting years, to get a clear idea of the history of medicine. Read Foster's *Lectures on the History of Physiology* and Baas's *History of Medicine*. Get the "Masters of Medicine" Series, and subscribe to the *Library and Historical Journal*.*

Every day do some reading or work apart from your profes- sion. I fully realize, no one more so, how absorbing is the profession of medicine; how applicable to it is what Michel- angelo says: "There are sciences which demand the whole of a man, without leaving the least portion of his spirit free for other distractions"; but you will be a better man and not a worse practitioner for an avocation. I care not what it may be; gar- dening or farming, literature or history or bibliography, any one of which will bring you into contact with books. (I wish that time permitted me to speak of the other two rooms which are really of equal importance with the library, but which are more difficult to equip, though of co-ordinate value in the ed-

* Brooklyn. Price $2 per annum.

ucation of the head, the heart, and the hand.) The third essential for the practitioner as a student is the quinquennial brain-dusting, and this will often seem to him the hardest task to carry out. Every fifth year, back to the hospital, back to the laboratory, for renovation, rehabilitation, rejuvenation, reintegration, resuscitation, etc. Do not forget to take the notebooks with you, or the sheets, in three separate bundles, to work over. From the very start begin to save for the trip. Deny yourself all luxuries for it; shut up the room you meant for the nursery—have the definite determination to get your education thoroughly well started; if you are successful you may, perhaps, have enough saved at the end of three years to spend six weeks in special study; or in five years you may be able to spend six months. Hearken not to the voice of old "Dr. Hayseed," who tells you it will ruin your prospects, and that he "never heard of such a thing" as a young man, not yet five years in practice, taking three months' holiday. To him it seems preposterous. Watch him wince when you say it is a speculation in the only gold mine in which the physician should invest—*Grey Cortex!* What about the wife and babies, if you have them? Leave them! Heavy as are your responsibilities to those nearest and dearest, they are outweighed by the responsibilities to yourself, to the profession, and to the public. Like Isaphaena, the story of whose husband—ardent, earnest soul, peace to his ashes!—I have told in the little sketch of *An Alabama Student,* your wife will be glad to bear her share in the sacrifice you make.

With good health and good habits the end of the second lustrum should find you thoroughly established—all three rooms well furnished, a good stable, a good garden, no mining stock, but a life insurance, and, perhaps, a mortgage or two on neighbouring farms. Year by year you have dealt honestly with yourself; you have put faithfully the notes of each case into their proper places, and you will be gratified to find that, though the doubtful cases and mistakes still make a rather formidable pile, it has grown relatively smaller. You literally "own" the countryside, as the expression is. All the serious and dubious cases come to you, and you have been so honest in the frank acknowledgement of your own mistakes, and so charitable in the contemplation of theirs, that neighbouring doctors, old and young, are glad to seek your advice. The work, which has been very heavy, is now lightened by a good assistant, one of your own students, who becomes in a year or so your partner. This is not an overdrawn picture, and it is one which may be seen in many places except, I am sorry to say, in the particular as to the partner. This is the type of man we need in the country districts and the smaller towns. He is not a whit too good to look after the sick, not a whit too highly educated—impossible! And with an optimistic temperament and a good digestion he is the very best product of our profession, and may do more to stop quackery and humbuggery, inside and outside of the ranks, than could a dozen prosecuting county attorneys. Nay, more! such a doctor may be a daily benediction in the community—a strong, sensible, whole-souled man, often living a life of great self-denial, and always of tender sympathy, worried neither by the vagaries of the well nor by the testy waywardness of the sick, and to him, if to any, may come (even when he knows it not) the true spiritual blessing—that "blessing which maketh rich and addeth no sorrow."

The danger in such a man's life comes with prosperity. He is safe in the hard-working day, when he is climbing the hill, but once success is reached, with it come the temptations to which many succumb. Politics has been the ruin of many country doctors, and often of the very best, of just such a good fellow as he of whom I have been speaking. He is popular; he has a little money; and he, if anybody, can save the seat for the party! When the committee leaves you, take the offer under consideration, and if in the ten or twelve years you have kept on intimate terms with those friends of your student days, Montaigne and Plutarch, you will know what answer to return. If you live in a large town, resist the temptation to open a sanatorium. It is not the work for a general practitioner, and there are risks that you may sacrifice your independence and much else besides. And, thirdly, resist the temptation to move into a larger place. In a good agricultural district, or in a small town, if you handle your resources aright, taking good care of your education, of your habits, and of your money, and devoting part of your energies to the support of the societies, etc., you may reach a position in the community of which any man

may be proud. There are country practitioners among my friends
with whom I would rather change places than with any in our
ranks, men whose stability of character and devotion to duty
make one proud of the profession.

Curiously enough, the student-practitioner may find stu-
diousness to be a stumbling-block in his career. A bookish man
may never succeed; deep-versed in books, he may not be able
to use his knowledge to practical effect; or, more likely, his
failure is not because he has studied books much, but because
he has not studied men more. He has never got over that
shyness, that diffidence, against which I have warned you. I
have known instances in which this malady was incurable; in
others I have known a cure effected not by the public, but by
the man's professional brethren, who, appreciating his work,
have insisted upon utilizing his mental treasures. It is very hard
to carry student habits into a large city practice; only zeal, a
fiery passion, keeps the flame alive, smothered as it is so apt
to be by the dust and ashes of the daily routine. A man may
be a good student who reads only the book of nature. Such a
one* I remember in the early days of my residence in Montreal—
a man whose devotion to patients and whose kindness and skill
quickly brought him an enormous practice. Reading in his car-
riage and by lamplight at Lucina's bedside, he was able to keep
well informed; but he had an insatiable desire to know the true
inwardness of a disease, and it was in this way I came into
contact with him. Hard pushed day and night, yet he was never
too busy to spend a couple of hours with me searching for data
which had not been forthcoming during life, or helping to un-
ravel the mysteries of a new disease, such as pernicious an-
aemia.

III

The *student-specialist* has to walk warily, as with two advantages there are two great dangers against which he has constantly to be on guard. In the bewildering complexity of modern

* The late John Bell.

medicine it is a relief to limit the work of a life to a comparatively narrow field which can be thoroughly tilled. To many men there is a feeling of great satisfaction in the mastery of a small department, particularly one in which technical skill is required. How much we have benefited from this concentration of effort in dermatology, laryngology, opthalmology, and in gynecology! Then, as a rule, the specialist is a free man, with leisure or, at any rate, with some leisure; not the slave of the public, with the incessant demands upon him of the general practitioner. He may live a more rational life, and has time to cultivate his mind, and he is able to devote himself to public interests and to the welfare of his professional brethren, on whose suffrages he so largely depends. How much we are indebted in the larger cities to the disinterested labours of this favoured class the records of our libraries and medical societies bear witness. The dangers do not come to the strong man in a speciality, but to the weak brother who seeks in it an easier field in which specious garrulity and mechanical dexterity may take the place of solid knowledge. All goes well when the man is larger than his speciality and controls it, but when the speciality runs away with the man there is disaster, and a topsy-turvy condition which, in every branch, has done incalculable injury. Next to the danger from small men is the serious risk of the loss of perspective in prolonged and concentrated effort in a narrow field. Against this there is but one safeguard—the cultivation of the sciences upon which the speciality is based. The student-specialist may have a wide vision—no student wider—if he gets away from the mechanical side of the art, and keeps in touch with the physiology and pathology upon which his art depends. More than any other of us, he needs the lessons of the laboratory, and wide contact with men in other departments may serve to correct the inevitable tendency to a narrow and perverted vision, in which the life of the anthill is mistaken for the world at large.

Of the *student-teacher* every faculty affords examples in varying degrees. It goes without saying that no man can teach successfully who is not at the same time a student. Routine, killing routine, saps the vitality of many who start with high aims, and who, for years, strive with all their energies against the degeneration which it is so prone to entail. In the smaller schools isolation, the absence of congenial spirits working at the same subject, favours stagnation, and after a few years the fires of early enthusiasm no longer glow in the perfunctory lectures. In many teachers the ever-increasing demands of practice leave less and less time for study, and a first-class man may lose touch with his subject through no fault of his own, but through an entanglement in outside affairs which he deeply regrets yet cannot control. To his five natural senses the student-teacher must add two more—the sense of responsibility and the sense of proportion. Most of us start with a highly developed sense of the importance of the work, and with a desire to live up to the responsibilities entrusted to us. Punctuality, the class first, always and at all times; the best that a man has in him, nothing less; the best the profession has on the subject, nothing less; fresh energies and enthusiasm in dealing with dry details; animated, unselfish devotion to all alike; tender consideration for his assistants—these are some of the fruits of a keen sense of responsibility in a good teacher. The sense of proportion is not so easy to acquire, and much depends on the training and on the natural disposition. There are men who never possess it; to others it seems to come naturally. In the most careful ones it needs constant cultivation—*nothing over-much* should be the motto of every teacher. In my early days I came under the influence of an ideal student-teacher, the late Palmer Howard, of Montreal. If you ask what manner of man he was, read Matthew Arnold's noble tribute to his father in his well-known poem, *Rugby Chapel*. When young, Dr. Howard had chosen a path—"path to a clear-purposed goal," and he pursued it with unswerving devotion. With him the study and the teaching of medicine were an absorbing passion, the ardour of which neither the incessant and ever-increasing demands upon his time nor the growing years could quench. When I first, as a senior student, came into intimate contact with him in the summer of 1871, the problem of tuberculosis was under discussion, stirred up by the epoch-making work of Villemin and the radical views of Niemeyer. Every lung lesion at the Montreal General

Hospital had to be shown to him, and I got my first-hand introduction to Laennec, to Graves, and to Stokes, and became familiar with their works. No matter what the hour, and it usually was after 10 p.m., I was welcome with my bag, and if Wilks and Moxon, Virchow, or Rokitanski gave us no help, there were the Transactions of the Pathological Society and the big *Dictionnaire* of Dechambre. An ideal teacher because a student, ever alert to the new problems, an indomitable energy enabled him in the midst of an exacting practice to maintain an ardent enthusiasm, still to keep bright the fires which he had lighted in his youth. Since those days I have seen many teachers, and I have had many colleagues, but I have never known one in whom was more happily combined a stern sense of duty with the mental freshness of youth.

But as I speak, from out the memory of the past there rises before me a shadowy group, a long line of students whom I have taught and loved, and who have died prematurely—mentally, morally, or bodily. To the successful we are willing and anxious to bring the tribute of praise, but none so poor to give recognition to the failures. From one cause or another, perhaps because when not absorbed in the present, my thoughts are chiefly in the past, I have cherished the memory of many young men whom I have loved and lost. *Io victis:* let us sometimes sing of the vanquished. Let us sometimes think of those who have fallen in the battle of life, who have striven and failed, who have failed even without the strife. How many have I lost from the student band by mental death, and from so many causes— some stillborn from college, others dead within the first year of infantile marasmus, while mental rickets, teething, tabes, and fits have carried off many of the most promising minds! Due to improper feeding within the first five fateful years, scurvy and rickets head the mental mortality bills of students. To the teacher-nurse it is a sore disappointment to find at the end of ten years so few minds with the full stature, of which the early days gave promise. Still, so widespread is mental death that we scarcely comment upon it in our friends. The real tragedy is the moral death which, in different forms, overtakes so many good fellows who fall away from the pure, honourable, and righteous service of Minerva into the idolatry of Bacchus, of Venus, or of Circe. Against the background of the past these tragedies stand out, lurid and dark, and as the names and faces of my old boys recur (some of them my special pride), I shudder to think of the blighted hopes and wrecked lives, and I force my memory back to those happy days when they were as you are now, joyous and free from care, and I think of them on the benches, in the laboratories, and in the wards—and there I leave them. Less painful to dwell upon, though associated with a more poignant grief, is the fate of those whom physical death has snatched away in the bud or blossom of the student life. These are among the tender memories of the teacher's life, of which he does not often care to speak, feeling with Longfellow that the surest pledge of their remembrance is "the silent homage of thoughts unspoken." As I look back it seems now as if the best of us had died, that the brightest and the keenest had been taken and the more commonplace among us had been spared. An old mother, a devoted sister, a loving brother, in some cases a brokenhearted wife, still pay the tribute of tears for the untimely ending of their high hopes, and in loving remembrance I would mingle mine with theirs. What a loss to our profession have been the deaths of such true disciples as Zimmerman, of Toronto; of Jack Cline and of R. L. MacDonnell, of Montreal; of Fred Packard and of Kirkbride, of Philadelphia; of Livingood, of Lazear, of Oppenheimer, and of Oechsner, in Baltimore—cut off with their leaves still in the green, to the inconsolable grief of their friends!

To each one of you the practice of medicine will be very much as you make it—to one a worry, a care, a perpetual annoyance; to another, a daily joy and a life of as much happiness and usefulness as can well fall to the lot of man. In the student spirit you can best fulfil the high mission of our noble calling—in his *humility*, conscious of weakness, while seeking strength; in his *confidence*, knowing the power, while recognizing the limitations of his art, in his *pride* in the glorious heritage from which the greatest gifts to man have been derived; and in his sure and certain hope that the future holds for us richer blessings than the past.

A BACKWOOD PHYSIOLOGIST*

The essay, "William Beaumont. A Pioneer American Physiologist," was first published in the Journal of the American Medical Association *(vol. 39, pages 1223–1231, 1902), and was reprinted in* An Alabama Student and Other Biographical Essays *(Oxford University Press, 1908), under the title, "A Backwood Physiologist." It appeared again in 1929 as the introduction to a reprint edition of Beaumont's* Experiments and Observations *(XIIIth International Physiological Congress, Boston, 1929).*

COME with me for a few moments on a lovely June day in 1822, to what were then far-off northern wilds, to the island of Michilimacinac, where the waters of Lake Michigan and Lake Huron unite and where stands Fort Mackinac, rich in the memories of Indian and voyageur, one of the four important posts on the upper lakes in the days when the rose and the fleur-de-lis strove for the mastery of the western world. Here the noble Marquette laboured for his Lord, and here beneath the chapel of St. Ignace they laid his bones to rest. Here the intrepid La Salle, the brave Tonty and the resolute Du Luht had halted in their wild wanderings. Its palisades and block-houses had echoed the war-whoops of Ojibwas and Ottawas, of Hurons and Iroquois, and the old fort had been the scene of bloody massacres and hard-fought fights; but at the conclusion of the War of 1812, after two centuries of struggle, peace settled at last on the island. The fort was occupied by United States troops, who kept the Indians in check and did general police duty on the frontier, and the place had become a rendezvous for Indians and voy-

* An Address before the St. Louis Medical Society, October 4, 1902.

ageurs in the employ of the American Fur Company. On this bright spring morning the village presented an animated scene. The annual return tide to the trading post was in full course, and the beach was thronged with canoes and batteaux laden with the pelts of the winter's hunt. Voyageurs and Indians, men, women, and children, with here and there a few soldiers, made up a motley crowd. Suddenly from the company's store there is a loud report of a gun, and amid the confusion and excitement the rumour spreads of an accident, and there is a hurrying of messengers to the barracks for a doctor. In a few minutes (Beaumont says twenty-five or thirty, an eyewitness says three) an alert-looking man in the uniform of a U.S. Army surgeon made his way through the crowd, and was at the side of a young French Canadian who had been wounded by the discharge of a gun, and with a composure bred of an exceptional experience of such injuries, prepared to make the examination. Though youthful in appearance, Surgeon Beaumont had seen much service, and at the capture of York and at the investment of Plattsburgh he had shown a coolness and bravery under fire which had won high praise from his superior officers. The man and the opportunity had met—the outcome is my story of this evening.

I. THE OPPORTUNITY—ALEXIS ST. MARTIN

On the morning of June 6 a young French Canadian, Alexis St. Martin, was standing in the company's store, 'where one of the party was holding a shotgun (not a musket), which was accidentally discharged, the whole charge entering St. Martin's body. The muzzle was not over three feet from him—I think not more than two. The wadding entered, as well as pieces of his clothing; his shirt took fire; he fell, as we supposed, dead.

'Doctor Beaumont, the surgeon of the fort, was immediately sent for, and reached the wounded man in a very short time, probably three minutes. We had just gotten him on a cot, and were taking off some of his clothing. After the doctor had extracted part of the shot, together with pieces of clothing, and dressed his wound carefully, Robert Stuart and others assisting, he left him, remarking, "The man cannot live thirty-six hours; I will come and see him by and by." In two or three hours he visited him again, expressing surprise at finding him doing better than he had anticipated. The next day, after getting out more shot and clothing, and cutting off ragged edges of the wound, he informed Mr. Stuart, in my presence, that he thought he would recover.'*

The description of the wound has been so often quoted as reported in Beaumont's work, that I give here the interesting summary which I find in a 'Memorial' presented to the Senate and House of Representatives by Beaumont:

'The wound was received just under the left breast, and supposed, at the time, to have been mortal. A large portion of the side was blown off, the ribs fractured, and openings made into the cavities of the chest and abdomen, through which protruded portions of the lungs and stomach, much lacerated and burnt, exhibiting altogether an appalling and hopeless case. The diaphragm was lacerated, and a perforation made directly into the cavity of the stomach, through which food was escaping at the time your memorialist was called to his relief. His life was at first wholly despaired of, but he very unexpectedly survived the immediate effects of the wound, and necessarily continued a long time under the constant professional care and treatment of your memorialist, and, by the blessing of God, finally recovered his health and strength.

'At the end of about ten months the wound was partially healed, but he was still an object altogether miserable and

---

* Statement of G. G. Hubbard, an officer of the company, who was present when St. Martin was shot, quoted by Dr. J. R. Baily, of Mackinac Island, in his address on the occasion of the Beaumont Memorial Exercises, Mackinac Island, July 10, 1900. *The Physician and Surgeon*, December, 1900.

helpless. In this situation he was declared "a common pauper" by the civil authorities of the county, and it was resolved by them that they were not able, nor required, to provide for or support, and finally declined taking care of him, and, in pursuance of what they probably believed to be their public duty, authorized by the laws of the territory, were about to transport him, in this condition, to the place of his nativity in lower Canada, a distance of more than fifteen hundred miles.

'Believing the life of St. Martin must inevitably be sacrificed if such attempt to remove him should be carried into execution at that time, your memorialist, after earnest, repeated, but unavailing, remonstrances against such a course of proceedings, resolved, as the only way to rescue St. Martin from impending misery and death, to arrest the process of transportation and prevent the consequent suffering, by taking him into his own private family, where all the care and attention were bestowed that his condition required.

'St. Martin was, at this time, as before intimated, altogether helpless and suffering under the debilitating effects of his wounds—naked and destitute of everything. In this situation your memorialist received, kept, nursed, medically and surgically treated and sustained him, at much inconvenience and expense, for nearly two years, dressing his wounds daily, and for considerable part of the time twice a day, nursed him, fed him, clothed him, lodged him and furnished him with such necessaries and comforts as his condition and suffering required.

'At the end of these two years he had become able to walk and help himself a little, though unable to provide for his own necessities. In this situation your memorialist retained St. Martin in his family for the special purpose of making physiological experiments.'

In the month of May, 1825, Beaumont began the experiments.

In June he was ordered to Fort Niagara, where, taking the man with him, he continued the experiments until August. He then took him to Burlington and to Plattsburgh. From the latter place St. Martin returned to Canada, without obtaining Dr. Beaumont's consent. He remained in Canada four years, worked as a voyageur, married and had two children. In 1829 Beaumont succeeded in getting track of St. Martin, and the American Fur Company engaged him and transported him to Fort Crawford on the upper Mississippi. The side and wound were in the same condition as in 1825. Experiments were continued uninterruptedly until March 1831, when circumstances made it expedient that he should return with his family to lower Canada. The 'circumstances', as we gather from letters, were the discontent and homesickness of his wife. As illustrating the mode of travel, Beaumont states that St. Martin took his family in an open canoe 'via the Mississippi, passing by St. Louis, ascended the Ohio river, then crossed the state of Ohio to the lakes, and descended the Erie and Ontario and the river St. Lawrence to Montreal, where they arrived in June.' Dr. Beaumont often lays stress on the physical vigour of St. Martin as showing how completely he had recovered from the wound. In November, 1832, he again engaged himself to submit to another series of experiments in Plattsburgh and Washington. The last recorded experiment is in November, 1833.

Among the Beaumont papers, for an examination of which I am much indebted to his daughter, Mrs. Keim, there is a large mass of correspondence relating to St. Martin, extending from 1827, two years after he had left the doctor's employ, to October, 1852. Alexis was in Dr. Beaumont's employ in the periods already specified. In 1833 he was enrolled in the United States Army at Washington as Sergeant Alexis St. Martin, of a detachment of orderlies stationed at the War Department. He was then twenty-eight years of age, and was five feet five inches in height.

Among the papers there are two articles of agreement, both signed by the contracting parties, one dated Oct. 19, 1833, and the other November 7 of the same year. In the former he bound himself for a term of one year to:

'Serve, abide and continue with the said William Beaumont, wherever he shall go or travel or reside in any part of the world his covenant servant and diligently and faithfully, etc.,. . . that he, the said Alexis, will at all times during said term when thereto directed or required by said William, submit to assist and promote by all means in his power such philosophical or medical experiments as the said William shall direct or cause to be made on or in the stomach of him, the said Alexis, either through and by means of the aperture or opening thereto in the side of him, the said Alexis, or otherwise, and will obey, suffer and comply with all reasonable and proper orders of or experiments of the said William in relation thereto and in relation to the exhibiting and showing of his said stomach and the powers and properties thereto and of the appurtenances and the powers, properties, and situation and state of the contents thereof.'

The agreement was that he should be paid his board and lodging and $150 for the year. In the other agreement it is for two years, and the remuneration $400. He was paid a certain amount of the money down.

There are some letters from Alexis himself, all written for him and signed with his mark. In June, 1834, he writes that his wife was not willing to let him go, and thinks that he can do a great deal better to stay at home. From this time on Alexis was never again in Dr. Beaumont's employ.

There is a most interesting and protracted correspondence in the years 1836, 1837, 1838, 1839, 1840, 1842, 1846, 1851 and 1852, all relating to attempts to induce Alexis to come to St. Louis. For the greater part of this time he was in Berthier, in the district of Montreal, and the correspondence was chiefly conducted with a Mr. William Morrison, who had been in the northwest fur trade, and who took the greatest interest in Alexis, and tried to induce him to go to St. Louis.

In 1846 Beaumont sent his son Israel for Alexis, and in a letter dated August 9, 1846, his son writes from Troy: 'I have just returned from Montreal, but without Alexis. Upon arriving at Berthier I found that he owned and lived on a farm about fifteen miles south-west of the village.' Nothing would induce him to go.

The correspondence with Mr. Morrison in 1851 and 1852 is most voluminous, and Dr. Beaumont offered Alexis $500 for the year, with comfortable support for his family. He agreed at one time to go, but it was too late in the winter and he could not get away.

The last letter of the series is dated Oct. 15, 1852, and is from Dr. Beaumont to Alexis, whom he addresses as *Mon Ami*. Two sentences in this are worth quoting:

'Without reference to past efforts and disappointments— or expectation of ever obtaining your services again for the purpose of experiments, etc., upon the proposals and conditions heretofore made and suggested, I now proffer to you in faith and sincerity, new, and I hope satisfactory, terms and conditions to ensure your prompt and faithful compliance with my most fervent desire to have you again with me—not only for my own individual gratification, and the benefits of medical science, but also for your own family's present good and future welfare.' He concludes with, 'I can say no more, Alexis—you know what I *have* done for you many years since—what I have been *trying,* and am still anxious and wishing to do with and for you— what efforts, anxieties, anticipations, and disappointments I have suffered from your non-fulfilment of my expectations. Don't disappoint me more nor forfeit the bounties and blessings reserved for you.'

So much interest was excited by the report of the experiments that it was suggested to Beaumont that he should take Alexis to Europe and submit him there to a more extended series of observations by skilled physiologists. Writing June 10, 1833, he says: 'I shall engage him for five or six years if he will agree, of which I expect there is no doubt. He has always been pleased with the idea of going to France. I feel much gratified at the expression of Mr. Livingston's desire that we should visit Paris, and shall duly consider the interest he takes in the subject and make the best arrangements I can to meet his views and yours.' Mr. Livingston, the American minister, wrote from Paris, March 18, 1834, saying that he had submitted the work to Orfila and the Academy of Sciences, which had appointed a committee to determine if additional experiments were necessary, and whether it was advisable to send to America for Alexis. Nothing, I believe, ever came of this, nor, so far as I can find, did Alexis visit Paris. Other attempts were made to secure him for pur- poses of study. In 1840 a student of Dr. Beaumont's, George Johnson, then at the University of Pennsylvania, wrote saying that Dr. Jackson had told him of efforts made to get Alexis to London, and Dr. Gibson informed him that the Medical Society of London had raised £300 or £400 to induce St. Martin to come, and that he, Dr. Gibson, had been trying to find St. Martin for his London friends. There are letters in the same year from Dr. R. D. Thomson, of London, to Professor Silliman, urging him to arrange that Dr. Beaumont and Alexis should visit London. In 1856 St. Martin was under the observation of Dr. Francis Gurney Smith, in Philadelphia, who reported a brief series of experiments, so far as I know the only other report made on him.*

St. Martin had to stand a good deal of chaffing about the hole in his side. His comrades called him 'the man with a lid on his stomach'. In his memorial address, Mr. C. S. Osborn, of Sault Ste. Marie, states that Miss Catherwood tells a story of Étienne St. Martin fighting with Charlie Charette because Charlie rid- iculed his brother. Étienne stabbed him severely, and swore that he would kill the whole brigade if they did not stop deriding his brother's stomach.

At one time St. Martin travelled about exhibiting the wound to physicians, medical students, and before medical societies.

* *Medical Examiner*, 1856, and *Experiments on Digestion*, Philadelphia, 1856.

In a copy of Beaumont's work, formerly belonging to Austin Flint, Jr., and now in the possession of a physician of St. Louis, there is a photograph of Alexis sent to Dr. Flint. There are statements made that he went to Europe, but of such a visit I can find no record.

My interest in St. Martin was of quite the general character of a teacher of physiology, who every session referred to his remarkable wound and showed Beaumont's book with the illustration. In the spring of 1880, while still a resident of Montreal, I saw a notice in the newspapers of his death at St. Thomas. I immediately wrote to a physician and to the parish priest, urging them to secure me the privilege of an autopsy, and offering to pay a fair sum for the stomach, which I agreed to place in the Army Medical Museum in Washington, but without avail. Subsequently, through the kindness of the Hon. Mr. Justice Baby, I obtained the following details of St. Martin's later life. Judge Baby writes to his friend, Prof. D. C. MacCallum of Montreal, as follows:

'I have much pleasure to-day in placing in your hands such information about St. Martin as Revd. Mr. Chicoine, Curé of St. Thomas, has just handed over to me. Alexis Bidigan, *dit* St. Martin, died at St. Thomas de Joliette on the 24th of June, 1880, and was buried in the cemetery of the parish on the 28th of the same month. The last sacraments of the Catholic church were ministered to him by the Revd. Curé Chicoine, who also attended at his burial service. The body was then in such an advanced stage of decomposition that it could not be admitted into the church, but had to be left outside during the funeral service. The family resisted all requests—most pressing as they were—on the part of the members of the medical profession for an autopsy, and also kept the body at home much longer than usual and during a hot spell of weather, so as to allow decomposition to set in and baffle, as they thought, the doctors of the surrounding country and others. They had also the grave dug eight feet below the surface of the ground in order to prevent any attempt at a resurrection. When he died St. Martin was 83 years of age, and left a widow, whose maiden name was Marie Joly. She survived him by nearly seven years, dying at St. Thomas on the 20th of April, 1887, at the very old age of 90 years. They left four children, still alive—Alexis, Charles, Henriette, and Marie.

'Now I may add the following details for myself. When I came to know St. Martin it must have been a few years before his death. A lawsuit brought him to my office here in Joliette. I was seized with his interests; he came to my office a good many times, during which visits he spoke to me at great length of his former life, how his wound had been caused, his peregrinations through Europe and the United States, etc. He showed me his wound. He complained bitterly of some doctors who had awfully misused him, and had kind words for others. He had made considerable money during his tours, but had expended and thrown it all away in a frolicsome way, especially in the old country. When I came across him he was rather poor, living on a small, scanty farm in St. Thomas, and very much addicted to drink, almost a drunkard one might say. He was a tall, lean man, with a very dark complexion, and appeared to me then of a morose disposition.'

II. The Book

In the four periods in which Alexis had been under the care and study of Beaumont a large series of observations had been recorded, amounting in all to 238. A preliminary account of the case, and of the first group of observations, appeared in the *Philadelphia Medical Recorder* in January, 1825. During the stay in Washington in 1832 the great importance of the observations had become impressed on the Surgeon-General, Dr. Lovell, who seems to have acted in a most generous and kindly spirit. Beaumont tried to induce him to undertake the arrangement of the observations, but Lovell insisted that he should do the work himself. In the spring of 1833 Alexis was taken to New York, and there shown to the prominent members of the profession, and careful drawings and coloured sketches were made of the wound by Mr. King. A prospectus of the work was issued and was distributed by the Surgeon-General, who speaks in a letter of sending them to Dr. Franklin Bache and to Dr. Stewart of Philadelphia, and in a letter from Dr. Bache to Dr. Beaumont, acknowledging the receipt of a bottle of gastric juice, Bache states that he has placed the prospectus in Mr. Judah Dobson's store, and has asked for subscribers. Beaumont did not find New York a very congenial place. He complained of the difficulty of doing the work, owing to the vexatious social intercourse. He applied for permission to go to Plattsburgh, in order to complete the book. After having made inquiries in New York and Philadelphia about terms of publication, he decided, as the work had to be issued at his own expense, that it could be as well and much more cheaply printed at Plattsburgh, where he would also have the advice and help of his cousin, Dr. Samuel Beaumont. In a letter to the Surgeon-General, dated June 10, 1833, he acknowledges the permission to go to Plattsburgh, and says: 'I shall make my arrangements to leave here for Pl. in about a week to *rush* the execution of the Book as fast as possible. I am now having the drawings taken by Mr. King engraved here.'

The summer was occupied in making a fresh series of experiments and getting the work in type. On December 3 he writes to the Surgeon-General that the book will be ready for distribution in a few days, and that 1,000 copies will be printed.

The work is an octavo volume of 280 pages, entitled *Experiments and Observations on the Gastric Juice and the Physiology of Digestion*, by William Beaumont, M.D., Surgeon in the United States Army. Plattsburgh. Printed by F. P. Allen, 1833. While it is well and carefully printed, the paper and type are not of the best, and one cannot but regret that Beaumont did not take the advice of Dr. Franklin Bache, who urged him strongly not to have the work printed at Plattsburgh, but in Philadelphia, where it could be done in very much better style. The dedication of the work to Joseph Lovell, M.D., Surgeon-General of the United States Army, acknowledges in somewhat laudatory terms the debt which Beaumont felt he owed to his chief, who very gratefully acknowledges the compliment and the kindly feeling, but characterizes the dedication as 'somewhat apocryphal'.

The work is divided into two main portions; first, the preliminary observations on the general physiology of digestion in seven sections: Section I, Of Aliment; Section II, Of Hunger and Thirst; Section III, Of Satisfaction and Satiety; Section IV, Of Mastication, Insalivation, and Deglutition; Section V, Of Digestion by the Gastric Juice; Section VI, Of the Appearance of the Villous Coat, and of the Motions of the Stomach; Section VII, Of Chylification and Uses of the Bile and Pancreatic Juice. The greater part of the book is occupied by the larger section of the detailed account of the four series of experiments and observations. The work concludes with a series of fifty-one inferences from the foregoing experiments and observations.

The subsequent history of the book itself is of interest, and may be dealt with here. In 1834 copies of the Plattsburgh edition, printed by F. P. Allen, were issued by Lilly, Wait & Co., of Boston.

In the Beaumont correspondence there are many letters from a Dr. McCall, in Utica, N.Y., who was an intimate friend of a Mr. Wm. Combe, a brother of the well-known physiologist and popular writer, Dr. Andrew Combe of Edinburgh. Doubtless it was through this connexion that in 1838 Dr. Combe issued an edition in Scotland, with numerous notes and comments.

The second edition was issued from Burlington, Vt., in 1847, with the same title-page, but after *Second Edition* there are the words, *Corrected by Samuel Beaumont, M.D.,* who was Dr. William Beaumont's cousin. In the preface to this edition the statement is made that the first edition, though a large one of 3,000 copies, had been exhausted. This does not agree with the statement made in a letter of Dec. 3, 1833, to the Surgeon-General, stating that the edition was to be 1,000 copies. Of course more may have been printed before the type was distributed. While it is stated to be a new and improved edition, so far as I can gather it is a verbatim reprint, with no additional observations, but with a good many minor corrections.

A German edition was issued in 1834, with the following title: *Neue Versuche und Beobachtungen über den Magensaft und die Physiologie der Verdauung, auf eine höchst merkwürdige Weise während einer Reihe von 7 Jahren an einem und demselben Subject angestellt.* Beaumont's earlier paper, already referred to, was abstracted in the *Magazin der ausländischen Litteratur der gesammten Heilkunde,* Hamburg, 1826, and also in the *Archives générales de Médecine,* Paris, 1828. I cannot find that there was a French edition of the work.

The *Experiments and Observations* attracted universal attention, both at home and abroad. The journals of the period contained very full accounts of the work, and within a few years the valuable additions to our knowledge filtered into the textbooks of physiology, which to-day in certain descriptions of the gastric juice and of the phenomena of digestion copy even the very language of the work.

III. THE VALUE OF BEAUMONT'S OBSERVATIONS

There had been other instances of artificial gastric fistula in man which had been made the subject of experimental study, but the case of St. Martin stands out from all others on account of the ability and care with which the experiments were conducted. As Dr. Combe says, the value of these experiments consists partly in the admirable opportunities for observation which Beaumont enjoyed, and partly in the candid and truth-seeking spirit in which all his inquiries seem to have been conducted. 'It would be difficult to point out any observer who excels him in devotion to truth, and freedom from the trammels of theory or prejudice. He tells plainly what he saw and leaves every one to draw his own inferences, or where he lays down conclusions he does so with a degree of modesty and fairness of which few perhaps in his circumstances would have been capable.'

To appreciate the value of Beaumont's studies it is necessary to refer for a few moments to our knowledge of the physiology of digestion in the year 1832, the date of the publication. Take, for example, 'The Work on Human Physiology' (published in the very year of the appearance of Beaumont's book), by Dunglison, a man of wide learning and thoroughly informed in the literature of the subject. The five or six old theories of stomach digestion, concoction, putrefaction, trituration, fermentation, and maceration, are all discussed, and William Hunter's pithy remark is quoted, 'some physiologists will have it, that the stomach is a mill, others, that it is a fermenting vat, others, again, that it is a stewpan; but, in my view of the matter, it is neither a mill, a fermenting vat, nor a stewpan; but a stomach, gentlemen, a stomach.'

The theory of chemical solution is accepted. This had been placed on a sound basis by the experiments of Reaumur, Spallanzani, and Stevens, while the studies of Tiedemann and Gmelin and of Prout had done much to solve the problems of the chemistry of the juice. But very much uncertainty existed as to the phenomena occurring during digestion in the stomach, the precise mode of action of the juice, the nature of the juice itself, and its action outside the body. On all these points the observations of Beaumont brought clearness and light where there had been previously the greatest obscurity.

The following may be regarded as the most important of the results of Beaumont's observations: First, the accuracy and completeness of description of the gastric juice itself. You will all recognize the following quotation, which has entered into the textbooks and passes current to-day:

'Pure gastric juice, when taken directly out of the stomach of a healthy adult, unmixed with any other fluid, save a portion of the mucus of the stomach with which it is most commonly and perhaps always combined, is a clear, transparent fluid; inodorous; a little saltish, and very perceptibly acid. Its taste, when applied to the tongue, is similar to this mucilaginous water slightly acidulated with muriatic acid. It is readily diffusible in water, wine, or spirits; slightly effervesces with alkalis; and is an effectual solvent of the *materia alimentaria*. It possesses the property of coagulating albumen, in an eminent degree; is powerfully antiseptic, checking the putrefaction of meat; and effectually restorative of healthy action, when applied to old, fetid sores and foul, ulcerating surfaces.'

Secondly, the confirmation of the observation of Prout that the important acid of the gastric juice was the muriatic or hydrochloric. An analysis of St. Martin's gastric juice was made by Dunglison, at that time a professor in the University of Virginia, and by Benjamin Silliman of Yale, both of whom determined the presence of free hydrochloric acid. A specimen was sent to the distinguished Swedish chemist, Berzelius, whose report did not arrive in time to be included in the work. In a letter dated July 19, 1834, he writes to Professor Silliman that he had not been able to make a satisfactory analysis of the juice. The letter is published in *Silliman's Journal*, vol. xxvii, July, 1835.

Thirdly, the recognition of the fact that the essential elements of the gastric juice and the mucus were separate secretions.

Fourthly, the establishment by direct observation of the profound influence of mental disturbances on the secretion of the gastric juice and on digestion.

Fifthly, a more accurate and fuller comparative study of the digestion in the stomach with digestion outside the body, confirming in a most elaborate series of experiments the older observations of Spallanzani and Stevens.

Sixthly, the refutation of many erroneous opinions relating to gastric digestion, and the establishment of a number of minor points of great importance, such as, for instance, the rapid disappearance of water from the stomach through the pylorus, a point brought out by recent experiments, but insisted on and amply proved by Beaumont.

Seventhly, the first comprehensive and thorough study of

the motions of the stomach, observations on which, indeed, is based the most of our present knowledge.

And lastly, a study of the digestibility of different articles of diet in the stomach, which remains to-day one of the most important contributions ever made to practical dietetics.

The greater rapidity with which solid food is digested, the injurious effects on the stomach of tea and coffee, when taken in excess, the pernicious influence of alcoholic drinks on the digestion, are constantly referred to. An all-important practical point insisted on by Beaumont needs emphatic reiteration to this generation:

'The system requires much less than is generally supplied to it. The stomach disposes of a definite quantity. If more be taken than the actual wants of the economy require, the residue remains in the stomach and becomes a source of irritation and produces a consequent aberration of function, or passes into the lower bowel in an undigested state, and extends to them its deleterious influence. Dyspepsia is oftener the effect of over-eating and over-drinking than of any other cause.'

One is much impressed, too, in going over the experiments, to note with what modesty Beaumont refers to his own work. He speaks of himself as a humble 'inquirer after truth and a simple experimenter'.

'Honest objections, no doubt, are entertained against the doctrine of digestion by the gastric juice. That they are so entertained by these gentlemen I have no doubt. And I cheerfully concede to them the merit of great ingenuity, talents, and learning, in raising objections to the commonly received hypothesis, as well as ability in maintaining their peculiar opinions. But we ought not to allow ourselves to be seduced by the ingenuity of argument or the blandishments of style. Truth, like beauty, is "when unadorned adorned the most"; and in prosecuting these experiments and inquiries, I believe I have been guided by its light.

Facts are more persuasive than arguments, however ingeniously made, and by their eloquence I hope I have been able to plead for the support and maintenance of those doctrines which have had for their advocates such men as Sydenham, Hunter, Spallanzani, Richerand, Abernethy, Broussais, Philip, Paris, Bostock, the Heidelberg and Paris professors, Dunglison, and a host of other luminaries in the science of physiology.'

In reality Beaumont anticipated some of the most recent studies in the physiology of digestion. Doubtless many of you have heard of Professor Pawlow's, of St. Petersburg, new work on the subject. It has been translated into German, and I see that an English edition is advertised. He has studied the gastric juice in an isolated pouch, ingeniously made at the fundus of the stomach of the dog, from which the juice could be obtained in a pure state. One of his results is the very first announced by Beaumont, and confirmed by scores of observations on St. Martin, viz. that, as he says, 'the gastric juice never appears to be accumulated in the cavity of the stomach while fasting.' Pawlow has shown very clearly that there is a relation between the amount of food taken and the quantity of gastric juice secreted. Beaumont came to the same conclusion: 'when aliment is received the juice is given in exact proportion to its requirements for solution.' A third point on which Pawlow lays stress is the curve of secretion of the gastric juice, the manner in which it is poured out during digestion. The greatest secretion, he has shown, takes place in the earlier hours. On this point hear Beaumont: 'It (the gastric juice) then begins to exude from the proper vessels and increases in proportion to the quantity of aliment naturally required and received.' And again: 'When a due and moderate supply of food has been received it is probable that the whole quantity of gastric juice for its complete solution is secreted and mixed with it in a short time.' A fourth point, worked out beautifully by Pawlow, is the adaptation of the juice to the nature of the food; I do not see any reference to this by Beaumont, but there are no experiments more full than those in which he deals with the influence of exercise, weather, and the emotions on the quantity of the juice secreted.

IV. MAN AND DOCTOR

Sketches of Dr. Beaumont's life have appeared from time to time. There is a worthy memoir by Dr. T. Reyburn in the *St. Louis Medical and Surgical Journal,* 1854, and Dr. A. J. Steele, at the first annual commencement of the Beaumont Medical College, 1887, told well and graphically the story of his life. A few years ago Dr. Frank J. Lutz, of this city, sketched his life for the memorial meeting of the Michigan State Medical Society on the occasion of the dedication of a Beaumont monument.

Among the papers kindly sent to me by his daughter, Mrs. Keim, are many autobiographical materials, particularly relating to his early studies and to his work as a surgeon in the War of 1812. There is an excellent paper in the handwriting, it is said, of his son, giving a summary of the earlier period of his life. So far as I know this has not been published, and I give it in full:

'Dr. William Beaumont was born in the town of Lebanon, Conn., on the 21st day of November, A.D. 1785. His father was a thriving farmer and an active politician of the proud old Jeffersonian school, whose highest boast was his firm support and strict adherence to the honest principles he advocated. William was his third son, who, in the winter of 1806–7, in the 22nd year of his age, prompted by a spirit of independence and adventure, left the paternal roof to seek a fortune and a name. His outfit consisted of a horse and cutter, a barrel of cider, and one hundred dollars of hard-earned money. With this he started, laying his course northwardly, without any particular destination, Honour his rule of action, Truth his only landmark, and trust placed implicitly in Heaven. Traversing the western part of Massachusetts and Vermont in the spring of 1807 he arrived at the little village of Champlain, N.Y., on the Canada frontier—an utter stranger, friendless and alone. But honesty of purpose and true energy invariably work good results. He soon gained the people's confidence, and was entrusted with their village school, which he conducted about three years, devoting his leisure hours to the study of medical works from the library of Dr. Seth Pomeroy, his first patron. He then went over to St. Albans, Vt., where he entered the office of Dr. Benjamin Chandler and commenced a regular course of medical reading, which he followed for two years, gaining the utmost confidence and esteem of his kind preceptor and friends. About this time the war of 1812 commenced, and he applied for an appointment in the U.S. Army, successfully. He was appointed assistant-surgeon to the Sixth Infantry, and joined his regiment at Plattsburgh, N.Y., on the 13th of September, 1812. On the 19th of March, 1813, he marched from Plattsburgh with the First Brigade, for Sackett's Harbour, where they arrived on the 27th inst. Here he remained in camp till the 22nd of April, when he embarked with the troops on Lake Ontario. His journal will best tell this portion of his history:

' "April 22, 1813.—Embarked with Captain Humphreys, Walworth and Muhlenburg, and companies on board the schooner *Julia*. The rest of the brigade, and the Second, with Foresith's Rifle Regiment and the Eighth Artillery—on board a ship, brig, and schooner—remain in the harbour till next morning.

' "23rd.—11 o'clock a.m.—Weighs anchor and put out under the impression we were going to Kingston. Got out 15 or 20 miles—encountered a storm—wind ahead and the fleet returned to harbour.

' "24th.—6 o'clock a.m.—Put out with a fair wind—mild and pleasant—the fleet sailing in fine order.

' "26th.—Wind pretty strong—increasing—waves run high, tossing our vessels roughly. At half-past four pass the mouth of Niagara river. This circumstance baffles imagination as to where we are going—first impressed with the idea of Kingston—then to Niagara—but now our destination must be 'Little York.' At sunset came in view of York Town and the Fort, where we lay off some 3 or 4 leagues for the night.

' "27th.—Sailed into harbour and came to anchor a little below the British Garrison. Filled the boats and effected a landing, though not without difficulty and the loss of some men. The British marched their troops down the beach to cut us off as landing, and, though they had every advantage, they could not effect their design. A hot engagement ensued, in which the enemy lost nearly a third of their men, and were soon compelled to quit the field, leaving their dead and wounded strewn in every direction. They retired to the Garrison, but from the loss sustained in the engagement, the undaunted courage of our men, and the brisk firing from our fleet, with the 12 and 32-pounders, they were soon obliged to evacuate it and retreat with all possible speed. Driven to this alternative, they devised the inhuman project of blowing up their magazine, containing 300 pounds of powder, the explosion of which had wellnigh destroyed our army. Over 300 were wounded and about 60 killed on the spot, by stones of all dimensions falling, like a shower of hail, in the midst of our ranks. A most distressing scene ensues in the hospital. Nothing is heard but the agonizing groans and supplications of the wounded and the dying. The surgeons wade in blood, cutting off arms and legs and trepanning heads, while the poor sufferers cry, 'O, my God! Doctor, relieve me from this misery! I cannot live!' 'Twas enough to touch the veriest heart of steel and move the most relentless savage. Imagine the shocking scene, where fellow beings lie mashed and mangled—legs and arms broken and sundered—heads and bodies bruised and mutilated to disfigurement! My deepest sympathies were roused—I cut and slashed for 36 hours without food or sleep.

' "29th.—Dressed upwards of 50 patients—from simple contusions to the worst of compound fractures—more than half the latter. Performed two cases of amputation and one of trepanning. At 12 p.m. retired to rest my fatigued body and mind."

'One month after the taking of York he witnessed the storming of Fort George. The troops were transported from York to "Four-Mile Creek" (in the vicinity of Ft. George), where they encamped from the 10th of May to the 27th, when they advanced to the attack. His journal runs thus:

' "May 27 (1813).—Embarked at break of day—Col. Scott with 800 men, for the advanced guard, supported by the First Brigade, commanded by General Boyd, moved in concert with the shipping to the enemy's shore and landed under their battery and in front of their fire with surprising success, not losing more than 30 men in the engagement, though the enemy's whole force was placed in the most advantageous situation possible. We routed them from their chosen spot—drove them from the country and took possession of the town and garrison."

'On the 11th of September, 1814, he was at the Battle of Plattsburgh, still serving as assistant-surgeon, though doing all the duty of a full surgeon. At the close of the war, in 1815, when the army was cut down, he was retained in service, but resigned soon after, deeming himself unjustly treated by the government in having others, younger and less experienced, promoted over him.

'In 1816 he settled in Plattsburgh and remained there four years in successful practice. In the meantime his army friends had persuaded him to join the service again, and, having applied, he was reappointed, in 1820, and ordered to Ft. Mackinac as post-surgeon. At the end of the first year he obtained leave of absence, returned to Plattsburgh, and married one of the most amiable and interesting ladies of that place. (She still survives her honoured husband, and in her green old age is loved devotedly by all who know her.) He returned to Mackinac the same year, and in 1822 came in possession of Alexis St. Martin, the subject of his *Experiments on the Gastric Juice*. By the accidental discharge of his gun, while hunting, St. Martin had dangerously wounded himself in the abdomen and came under the treatment of Dr. Beaumont, who healed the wound (in itself a triumph of skill almost unequalled) and in 1825 commenced a series of experiments, the results of which have a world-wide publication. These experiments were continued, with various interruptions, for eight years, during which time he was ordered from post to post—now at Niagara, N.Y., anon at Green Bay, Mich., and finally at Fort Crawford, on the Mississippi. In 1834 he was ordered to St. Louis, where he remained in service till 1839, when he resigned. He then commenced service with the citizens of St. Louis, and from that time till the period of his last illness, enjoyed an extensive and distinguished practice, interrupted only by the base attacks of a few disgraceful and malicious knaves (self-deemed members of the medical profession) who sought to destroy a reputation which they could not share. They gained nothing except some little unenviable notoriety, and they have skulked away like famished wolves, to die in their hiding-places.'

The dates of Beaumont's commissions in the army are as follows: Surgeon's Mate, Sixth Regiment of Infantry, December 2, 1812; Cavalry, March 27, 1819; Post-Surgeon, December 4, 1819; Surgeon First Regiment and Surgeon, November 6, 1826.

From the biographical sketches of Reyburn, Steele, and Lutz, and from the personal reminiscences of his friends, Drs. J. B. Johnson, S. Pollak, and Wm. McPheeters, who fortunately remains with you, full of years and honours, we gather a clearly defined picture of the latter years of his life. It is that of a faithful, honest, hard-working practitioner, doing his duty to his patients, and working with zeal and ability for the best interests of the profession. The strong common sense which he exhibited in his experimental work made him a good physician and a trusty adviser in cases of surgery. Among his letters there are some interesting pictures of his life, particularly in his letters to his cousin, Dr. Samuel Beaumont. Writing to him April 4, 1846, he says:

'I have a laborious, lucrative, and increasing practice, more than I can possibly attend to, though I have an assistant, Dr. Johnson, a young man who was a pupil of mine from 1835 to 1840. He then went to Philadelphia a year or two to attend lectures, and graduated, and returned here again in 1842, and has been very busy ever since, and is so now, but notwithstanding I decline more practice daily than half the doctors in the city get in a week. You thought when you were here before that there was too much competition for you ever to think of succeeding in business here—there is ten times as much now, and the better I succeed and prosper for it. You must come with a different feeling from your former—with a determination to follow in my wake and stem the current that I will break for you. I am now in the grand climacteric of life, three-score years and over, with equal or more zeal and ability to do good and contribute to professional service than at forty-five, and I now look forward with pleasing anticipation of success and greater usefulness—have ample competence for ourselves and children, and no doleful or dreaded aspect of the future—to be sure I have to wrestle with some adverse circumstances of life, and more particularly to defend myself against the envious, mean, and professional jealousies and the consequent prejudices of some men, but I triumph over them all and go ahead in defiance of them.'*

His professional work increased enormously with the rapid growth of the city, but he felt, even in his old age, that delicious exhilaration which it is your pleasure and privilege to enjoy here in the west in a degree rarely experienced by your eastern confrères. Here is a cheery paragraph from a letter dated Oct. 20, 1852: 'Domestic affairs are easy, peaceable, and pleasant. Health of community good—no severe epidemic diseases prevalent—weather remarkably pleasant—business of all kinds in-

* He had evidently hopes that when his cousin and son arrived with Alexis they would arrange and plan for another series of experiments, and in another year or two make another book, better than the old one.

creasing—product of the earth abundant—money plenty—
railroads progressing with almost telegraphic speed—I expect
to come to Plattsburgh next summer all the way by rail.'

But work was becoming more burdensome to a man nearing
threescore years and ten, and he expresses it in another letter
when he says: 'There is an immense professional practice in
this city. I get tired of it, and have been trying hard to withdraw
from it altogether, but the more I try the tighter I seem to be
held to it by the people. I am actually persecuted, worried, and
almost worn out with valetudinarian importunities and hypo-
chondriacal groans, repinings, and lamentations—Amen.'

He continued at work until March, 1853, when he had an
accident—a fall while descending some steps. A few weeks later
a carbuncle appeared on the neck, and proved fatal, April 25.
One who knew him well wrote the following estimate (quoted
by Dr. F. J. Lutz in his sketch of Beaumont):

'He was gifted with strong natural powers, which, working upon an extensive experience in life, resulted in a spe-
cies of natural sagacity, which, as I suppose, was something
peculiar in him, and not to be attained by any course of
study. His temperament was ardent, but never got the
better of his instructed and disciplined judgement, and
whenever or however employed, he ever adopted the most
judicious means for attaining ends that were always honourable. In the sick room he was a model of patience and
kindness; his intuitive perceptions, guiding a pure benev-
olence, never failed to inspire confidence, and thus he
belonged to that class of physicians whose very presence
affords Nature a sensible relief.'

You do well, citizens of St. Louis and members of our profession, to cherish the memory of William Beaumont. Alive you
honoured and rewarded him, and there is no reproach against
you of neglected merit and talents unrecognized. The profession
of the northern part of the state of Michigan has honoured itself
in erecting a monument to his memory near the scene of his

disinterested labours in the cause of humanity and science. His name is linked with one of your educational institutions, and joined with that of a distinguished labourer in another field of practice. But he has a far higher honour than any you can give him here—the honour that can only come when the man and the opportunity meet—and match. Beaumont is the pioneer physiologist of this country, the first to make an important and enduring contribution to this science. His work remains a model of patient, persevering investigation, experiment, and research, and the highest praise we can give him is to say that he lived up to and fulfilled the ideals with which he set out, and which he expressed when he said: 'Truth, like beauty, is "when un-adorned, adorned the most", and, in prosecuting these experi-ments and inquiries, I believe I have been guided by its light.'[1]

---

[1] Some lengthy appendices, published in the original version, have been omitted in this edition. [C.G.R.]

William Osler with McGill
colleagues F. J. Shepherd
and George Ross (seated),
c. 1878

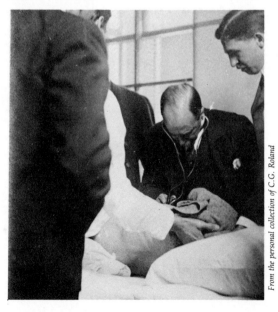

Osler on the wards at
Johns Hopkins, c. 1904

THE GROWTH OF A PROFESSION*

*Osler's presidential address to the Canadian Medical Association,
"On the Growth of a Profession," was published originally in the
Canada Medical & Surgical Journal (vol. 14, pages 129–155,
1885–86).*

GENTLEMEN: When I removed last year to another part of
the great field in which, without distinction of race or country, we are all laborers, it seemed good to you, fellow-workers,
in the kindness of your hearts, to nominate me President of the
Association. If in the tumult of thoughts which come tumbling
unbidden into a man's mind, the idea of such an honor ever
came, truly it was as a speck in the horizon of my ambition
towards which, as years rolled on, I might travel; but it has
been ordered otherwise, and as exceptional circumstances have
placed me in an exceptional position, I can but crave your in-
dulgence in the exercise of an office for which I feel that I lack
certain important qualifications.

Let me, in the first place, give expression to the general regret
that the Association has not been able to carry out its programme
and meet in Winnipeg as had been arranged, but with Mars in
the ascendant, and Big Bear and Poundmaker on the warpath,
our brethren of the prairie city thought it would be better—
perhaps safer—to postpone the meeting in the Northwest unto
a more convenient season, when grim-visaged war shall have
smoothed its wrinkled front. But, again, let me express the
satisfaction we feel at being able to meet here in Chatham among

* An Address, delivered at the Eighteenth Annual Meeting of the Canada
Medical Association, held at Chatham, Ontario, September 2 and 3, 1885.

men we know so well, who have been so faithful to the Association, and in a section of the country in which the profession possesses so many able and industrious members.

In seeking for a theme upon which to address you, I felt that if we met in Winnipeg, some subject connected with growth and development would alone be in keeping with the remarkable progress which the Northwest and its capital have made during the past decade. I thought that by tracing the lines along which the profession in a new country should advance, the meeting might perhaps help the movement and give a stimulus to thought and action, which is often one of the best effects of gatherings of this kind. When circumstances necessitated a change in the place of meeting, it seemed as if my subject, upon which I had spent some thought, should also be changed; but, on reflection, it was evident that the conditions in the older provinces were only an advanced stage of those existing in Winnipeg and Manitoba—progress should be our watchword here as there, growth and development the essential features of our professional life, and upon these topics I could as well address you in Ontario as in the Northwest. I want then to tell you, in as few words as possible, just how far on we have got and what have been the methods of our progress. In some parts of the Dominion we may study the profession in its simplest form; in the Northwest Territories, for example, it has not advanced beyond the amœba stage. The doctors there are so many unicellular creatures—masses of undifferentiated professional protoplasm, without organization or special functional activities. They cannot even exercise the rhizopodal mode of multiplication, but increase by the low inorganic method of accretion. In the older Provinces, on the other hand, the professional units have combined for the general good into a sort of polypidom— the organized profession—a great advance on the amœba stage; there are special organs of reproduction known as the medical schools, and there are signs of a nervous system—medical societies.

The three aspects then in the growth and development of the profession to which I wish to direct your attention, are (1) the organized profession; (2) the medical school; and (3) the medical society:

1. The organized profession. In a well-arranged community a citizen should feel that he can at any time command the services of a man who has received a fair training in the science and art of medicine, into whose hands he may commit with safety the lives of those near and dear to him. For the State to regulate and determine the individuals to whom the citizen may apply, is not by most persons thought unreasonable. There are those, however, who would have no restrictions, but allow the utmost freedom and permit assumption and assurance to have full sway, and give to any man without special education the right to practise medicine. This has never been the case in Canada. The men who came here in the early days to practise medicine were chiefly English and Scotch licentiates, who brought with them the traditions and customs of the profession in Great Britain. Very many of them were army surgeons, accustomed by long training to system and discipline. Without medical schools, the only recourse for a young man wishing to enter the profession was either to cross the ocean or to serve an apprenticeship with and receive instruction from a practitioner. Boards for the inspection of diplomas of men coming from outside the country and for the examination of the young men who had passed the necessary time with local preceptors, were organized in the old Province of Quebec in 1788, and in Upper Canada in 1815—dates ever to be memorable in the history of medicine in this country.

It is a common experience that men do not always appreciate their blessings and advantages. Those who are the best off are the least sensible of it. I have often thought this of the profession in Canada in relation to the Medical Boards, when I have heard murmurs of discontent. As they constitute a special feature in the Canadian medical system, you will allow me to refer to their origin and functions at some length. Primarily, the Medical Board is simply a Bureau of Registration appointed by the State, as, in fact, the British Medical Council is to-day; but here, at an early period, before the establishment of schools and universities, it was an examining body as well, and granted permits to practise. As universities sprang up, the latter part of the duties of the Medical Board was in part abrogated, and the functions more or less limited to the registration of degrees. An exceedingly important change was effected when the boards became elective bodies, truly representative of the profession. In Ontario, this was brought about by the Act of 1866, and in Quebec, by the Act of 1847. In this province the mode of selection of members is truly democratic, the profession in each electoral district selecting their candidate. In the province of Quebec a more cumbrous and less distinctly popular mode is followed, whereby each constituent of a district votes not only for his own, but for the candidates in all other districts. As proxies are allowed, the entire election may be in the hands of any clique collecting the largest number, but this method is doomed, and the more popular one will shortly be introduced.

The struggle has all along been between the universities and the profession, as represented by the Medical Boards. The former have always maintained the right of their alumni to license without further examination—a privilege still granted in the Province of Quebec. But the universities chartered by the crown in past days did more, they opposed bitterly the incorporation of independent medical schools, as witness the hostility to the Montreal School of Medicine by the McGill University, and to the Toronto School of Medicine by the University of Toronto. Much of this opposition was based on the highest motives. The opponents were afraid that if numerous independent schools arose, each with licensing power, and the license recognized by the Provincial Boards, that free trade in diplomas would result, the standard be lowered, and the profession, as a profession, ruined.

As at present constituted, the Medical Boards are entrusted by law with full power to regulate medical education in the provinces, to say what preliminary branches shall be required, of what the curriculum shall consist, and to make such changes as from time to time may seem advisable. When we consider the conditions under which we live, these enactments are in the highest degree advantageous. There are in the Dominion eleven medical schools, many of which are corporations without any control, with faculties irresponsible as regards supervision by trustees, censors, or governors. Even of those which form actual parts of universities, the faculties are partly or altogether independent, and there have been several instances in which, for greater freedom, the benefits of university connections have been sacrificed. The inevitable result of such a state of affairs is keen competition. The students are few, the schools are many; expenses are heavy, receipts are light; human nature is frail— what will follow you know—restrictions are relaxed, special inducements are offered, gradually the standard is lowered, the meshes are widened, examinations become a farce, and the schools degenerate into diploma mills, in which the highest interests of the profession and the safety of the public are prostituted to the cupidity of the owners. The depths to which unlicensed competition will sink the proprietors of some institutions, pass the comprehension of a right-minded person. They will compass heaven and earth to gain students, resorting to measures of solicitation and inducements, various tricks, and artifices which would be deemed doubtful in a grave-yard insurance company. Finally, upon the proprietors of such schools comes a sort of moral paralysis, such a condition as divines call the hardened heart; when, incapable of seeing, much less doing, the right, they believe the system in which they work is a true and good one, and attempts at reformation become well-nigh hopeless. The picture is not overdrawn. Unrestricted competition between numerous schools means free trade in diplomas, and free trade in this sense is synonymous with manslaughter.

From this disastrous condition the medical boards have saved Canadian schools. Bitterly did the colleges fight against increasing the powers of the boards; jealous in the extreme of their chartered rights; and too often eager in obstructing, instead of furthering, useful legislation, they have found, though they did not know it, victory in defeat. The principle is sound and well founded; the united profession of a country or a province should be the guardian of its own honor; greater than the schools, which are but a part of it. The control of all matters relating to medical education and practice may safely be entrusted to its care.

The incorporated body of the profession in each province of Canada is variously known as the "College of Physicians and Surgeons," the "Medical Council," or the "Medical Board," and, as you are all well aware, by the Act of Confederation, each province is left to regulate its own educational affairs.

Within the past ten or twelve years, so many important changes have been effected, particularly in the older provinces of Ontario and Quebec, that the boards are gradually approaching a state of efficiency.

As regards education, the ideal board should perform the following duties: 1st. Test the fitness of young men to enter upon the study of medicine; 2d. Order the curriculum in a manner best suited to the country and the requirements of modern medicine; and, 3d. Control absolutely the examinations for the license to practise. Upon each of these points I propose to make a few remarks, referring particularly to existing conditions:

1. Preliminary education and matriculation. In most of the provinces a thoroughly satisfactory system prevails, and a young man, before entering upon the study of medicine, must give evidence that his general education is of such a nature as will enable him to pursue intelligently the study of a learned profession. If the examination is satisfactory, he is permitted to register, and his studies date from this period. A board should control its own matriculation examination, and should accept no other. It is directly responsible to the profession that no incompetent person shall be admitted to study. The check comes lighter to a young man, and is more easily borne at this time than later in his career. The examiners should be independent persons, engaged in general teaching, and there should be at least three or four. No one man can conduct a preliminary examination with entire satisfaction. The organization of the board of matriculation examiners in Quebec should serve as a model for all the other provinces. It was a decidedly retrograde step when the medical council of this province relegated the entrance examination to other hands. And the acceptance of the intermediate High School certificate is not without its disadvantages. We want increasing watchfulness in this matter, and in the interests of higher education the boards should receive the cordial support of all the medical schools in their endeavours to effect an honest and satisfactory standard. That there has been laxity in the past, any one who has had to read many papers at examinations knows only too well. Throughout

Canada the subjects for matriculation have always closely followed those recommended by the British Medical Council, and embrace the elements of a good general education, with a fair amount of Latin. To these special subjects have lately been added Natural Philosophy, Chemistry, and Botany (optional). The student has had in the past several difficulties to contend with which should be removed. He has had to pass in some cases two examinations: one before the board of his province, and the other before the university at which he wishes to take his degree. Now the matriculation examination of the boards should be placed on such a level, and conducted in such a way, that any university could consistently accept it in lieu of its own, and if it was universally recognized by the profession, by teachers of high schools, and by the candidates, that there was but one portal of admission to the study of medicine, and that through the medical board by means of its authorized examiners, a great deal of trouble and annoyance would be prevented. Again, in the interests of the student, the greatest care should be exercised in the selection by the examiners of subjects which the candidates will find taught in the advanced classes of the high schools. Similar books to those read for other matriculations should as far as possible be chosen. Lack of attention to these apparently petty details has caused no little irritation on the part of students and teachers.

Let me, then, urge upon you the importance of doing all in your power to put the preliminary education of the student on a good basis; it is in your own hands—insist on competent independent boards, responsible to your chosen representatives; and, what is equally important, impress upon your students and the young men who seek your advice, the need of careful preparation. As a result of some years of observation, I should say that the general practitioners throughout the country are not quite alive to their duty in this matter. Too often young men go up for their examinations imperfectly prepared, and just slip through, to flounder on, hampered at every turn by defective preliminary training.

2. The regulation of the curriculum. The general profession, through its delegates, has an incontrovertible right to regulate

and frame the curriculum of study which men shall follow who aspire to join its ranks. The governments allow this right, and have empowered the Boards to frame such measures as they see fit. In the exercise of this function there has been a little friction in the past, and in no one of their duties will the Boards of the various provinces require to proceed with greater circumspection in the future. That there has been a good deal of tinkering, and not always of a satisfactory kind, is a complaint frequently made by schoolmen. That there has been very little and that the results have not been bad, will, I think, be the verdict of any one who looks into the matter fully. The curriculum is at present in a transition stage, and we must expect in the next few years to see important changes, but into these I do not propose to go in detail. One thing is clear, that the Boards and the teaching bodies must act in concert—in the interest of the student and of the profession harmonious action must be arranged. In this country the students of all classes seek the degree as well as the license and are not, as the majority are in Great Britain, satisfied with the latter. Hence the imperative need of a certain uniformity in the requirements of the boards of the universities. The teachers cannot possibly arrange the instruction on diverse plans. The duty of the Board is to lay down a minimum curriculum to which every student shall conform, and which the schools can easily carry out. The university requirements, while as much higher as the authorities chose to exact, should be laid down in the same lines, so that a student could easily proceed in his studies for the one or the other without inconvenience, and the teachers prepare a man for either examination without needless repetitions.

Fortunately the universities and teaching bodies are well represented—too well in Ontario in proportion to the territorial representatives—on the boards, and the introduction and regulation of the necessary changes in the curriculum will fall chiefly into the hands of their delegates, but there are many details which require careful attention on the part of all. The members of the educational committees of the boards have their work laid out for the next few years. Among important questions which await settlement in some of the Provinces are the

strict enforcement of the four years of study and the advisability of prolonging the session to nine months, or, what amounts to the same thing, making the summer session compulsory. The plan of allowing a student to pass one of his four years of study with a physician should be done away with at as early a date as possible. For two reasons: in the first place, it is, in a majority of instances, a farce, and we find on inquiry that the student has been pursuing his usual avocation, and perhaps going to a doctor's office in the evening: it is certainly not the equivalent of a session at college. If allowed at all, it should not be the first year, but the third, as permitted in the Province of Quebec, for then a student is in a position to obtain really valuable instruction in practical medicine and surgery from his preceptor. I was surprised, a few years ago, on obtaining the statistics from the registrar of one of the boards, to find how many men there were who passed on the three sessions. In this matter, the boards should not be behind the leading universities, which no longer recognize the year with a physician as the equivalent of a session. And, in the second place, the change should be made in the interests of the schools themselves. On no possible scheme can you arrange a satisfactory three-session course. Either a man pays too much attention to his primary subjects in the first two sessions and leaves the important final branches for one short session, or he tries in his second session to work hard at both and ends in a muddle-pated condition which unfits him for either. The prolongation of the session to nine months, as now exists in some of the schools in the Province of Quebec, must ultimately come in all the colleges. How the foolish habit arose of giving six months' vacation we need not stop to inquire—the folly of it is too evident to need remark; and we can safely predict that within ten years the nine months' course will be universal, either as a continuous session, as at Laval University, or by making the now optional summer session compulsory.

3. The control of the licensing power is the most important function of the medical boards. Acting on behalf of the State, it is their duty to see that all candidates for the license are properly qualified. They stand as the guardians of the public

and of the profession, and here their responsibilities are indeed great. In the ideal condition, there should be but one portal in each country through which a man can enter the profession and legally exercise its rights—a uniform standard of qualification to which each one must conform. This is secured in some countries by the direct action of the State, which appoints examiners for the purpose. But a better system is that which we have here reached, in which the State entrusts the incorporated profession with the duty. On this question the hottest battles of the profession have been and are being fought. The universities and chartered colleges have contested, inch by inch, the rights of the profession in this matter, and the struggle has not everywhere concluded. The possession of a degree in medicine from a university, no matter how reputable, cannot on any reasonable ground carry with it the right to registration and practise. The schools are independent bodies, outside, in a large measure, of State, and altogether of professional, control; they are numerous, and the competition between them is close; the requirements for graduation are variable, and the standard of examination unequal. They are close corporations, and neither the public nor the profession ever know what transpires in their councils. In the majority the teachers are also the examiners. Such a state of things can only lead to relaxation, and is fraught with danger to the best interests of all concerned.

A uniform system has not yet been adopted in all the provinces. In too many the possession of a degree, obtained after a proper course of study, still entitles the holder to the license, all others having to submit to examination. In the Province of Ontario the most advanced position has been reached, and the one road to registration is through the examination conducted by a board appointed by the medical council. To this the other provinces must ultimately come. It is what the profession in Great Britain has been striving after for years, and so far striving in vain against the power of corporations and vested interests. In the Province of Quebec the medical board accepts degrees from the local universities to which it sends assessors—after the manner of the British Medical Council, who report on the nature of the examinations. Others than the holders of such

degrees must submit to examination. Although this method has not worked badly, it is but a makeshift, and must finally be replaced by a central board of examiners, who shall test the qualifications of all candidates. Unfortunately the prevalent conditions of that province are such that dual boards will be needed, one for the French and one for the English.

In carrying out the details of a central examining board, there are inevitable difficulties which at first cause worry and discontent, but, with patience and mutual forebearance, gradually vanish. The choice of suitable examiners is a delicate matter, and one on which the schoolmen are apt to air grievances more or less just. They certainly should not be selected at random from the members of the council. A few years ago a friend of mine was nominated examiner in chemistry at the Quebec Board. He was a remarkably able practitioner, with a very indistinct and hazy knowledge of chemistry, and it was hard to say who was most uneasy at the examination, Dr.—or the students. Teachers in the schools have good grounds for complaint when the Boards select as examiner on special subjects—such as anatomy, chemistry, physiology, and pathology—men who have been for years in active practice without any possibility of keeping their own knowledge on these subjects fresh and practical, and who to "brush up" require to work as hard, may be, as the poor candidates. With the more practical branches these difficulties do not exist, and the Councils have a wide field for selection. Where special technical knowledge is needed, it would be preferable even to override the law which forbids the selection by the Boards of any teacher as an examiner on his own subject. For the "Staats Examen," in Germany, the professors in different departments are usually chosen by the government to conduct the examination in their special branches. The point is one to which the Boards should attend carefully in the future. They lose the respect of the profession and of the students in nominating as examiners men without special qualifications in certain fields.

The examinations for the license should be made in all respects as practical as possible, but to do this a Provincial Board must possess its own building and appliances, and make ar-

rangements with hospital authorities to have free access to a sufficient number of patients. As the work is done primarily in the interests of the public, it is clearly the duty of the Legislatures to assist in making suitable provision, and it seems probable that Ontario, the first to set the example of a one-portal licensing system, will also be the first to have a local habitation worthy of her incorporated profession. Such a building should contain the paraphernalia necessary for examination purposes. The division into a primary and a final examination, as at present made in most of our universities, and at the Ontario Medical Council, seems the best arrangement. The former embracing anatomy, physiology, general and medical chemistry, and materia medica; the latter, the practical branches of medicine, surgery, and midwifery. In practical details the "Staats-Examen," of Germany, might in many particulars be followed.

A serious difficulty has been felt in conducting the examinations satisfactorily as regards time, place, and rapidity. They should come off after the university examinations have been completed, and not, as now, immediately at the close of the session. More time could then be given, which will be necessary if the tests are to be made more practical. As the number of candidates increases, the examiners on each branch should be doubled. One centre in each province should be chosen for the sittings of the Board, and in almost each instance this will be the chief town. To go to Quebec for one meeting and Montreal the next, as is the practice in the Province of Quebec, and to hold an examination in Kingston as well as in Toronto, are touching and tender tributes to age with which a harder generation must soon dispense.

Very much more time must be hereafter given to those practical portions of the examinations which afford the only true test of a man's fitness to enter the profession. The day of theoretical examinations is over.

Permit me to refer to one or two other questions in connection with the medical boards. An anomaly which has been the source of no little irritation results from our close connection with the mother country. Any registered practitioner of Great Britain under the present British act can claim registration in the col-

onies without further examination. For some years Ontario contested the right but it was finally settled by the registration of Dr. E. St. G. Baldwin, in 1879, and Dr. A. E. Mallory, in 1880, since which time many have been entered on the register without examination. The Medical Bill which was shelved last year in the House of Commons contained a clause permitting the colonies to make any regulations they pleased concerning registration, and doubtless a similar proviso will appear in any future bill. The objections to receiving British registration are precisely those made against the reception of Canadian registration in Great Britain. The examinations are conducted by corporations with varied standards, of whose proceedings nothing is known, and over which no control can be exercised. But in Ontario the shoe pinches badly in another way. After graduating, students are enabled to give the Board the slip by taking an English or Scotch qualification, and registering in Great Britain, when they return and are entered upon the register without further examination. The objection to this lies in the fact that many men have evaded the just regulations of their province and returned with British registration, when even they could not have qualified for examination at the Ontario Medical Board. With few exceptions, Canadians seek in Great Britain the easier qualifications, particularly the license of Edinburgh Colleges. At some of these the custom has been with Canadian graduates to examine the parchment, accept the University degree, and admit the candidate to examination without any further inquiry. To avoid an injustice, the British licensing bodies must examine the matriculation certificate, and have satisfactory proof by class tickets that a student has spent four years in the study of medicine. Under these conditions registration in Ontario on a British certificate would be no hardship, though there would still be the unfair discrimination against the local institutions.

Through the kindness of Dr. Pyne, the Registrar, I am able to give you some figures bearing on this question. In the past five years 378 men have registered in the Province of Ontario, and of these there were 93 Canadians, who did so on their British registration; that is to say, about one-fourth of the number have avoided the enactments of the Board by proceeding to Great Britain and passing at one of the Colleges. No one can doubt that these 93 men were greatly benefited by the period of additional study and by contact with men of other schools and countries, but they would have been still more benefited if they had first conformed to the requirements of their own province, and aided the profession in maintaining regulations the benefits of which are universally recognized.

The fees demanded by the boards excite a good deal of grumbling on the part of students and practitioners. A sum of $70 is charged by the Ontario Board for the three examinations, matriculation, primary, and final; and in Quebec the registration fee is $20, and the matriculation $10. It is the old story, those who are best treated often complain the most. In the matter of fees, the medical students of Canada are in too easy a position, and they must expect changes in the near future. While the expenses of conducting a medical school have quadrupled in the past twenty-five years, the fees have not increased ten per cent. The charges of the boards are just and reasonable, as well as necessary to meet expenses. The annual tax on physicians of $1 in Ontario and $2 in Quebec, is often spoken of as irksome, but surely it is a trifling contribution to the general welfare of the profession.

It seems extraordinary to outsiders that in a country like Canada, with scarcely five millions of inhabitants, there should be so many licensing boards, and a still greater anomaly, that a licentiate in one province cannot practise in another—that there should be no reciprocity. So it seemed also to many earnest minds a decade or so ago, when in this Association a strong attempt was made at several meetings to frame a Dominion Medical Bill. It failed, as will, I think, subsequent ones, should they be made. Only one remedy remains, the boards of the various provinces may in time so assimilate the curriculum and examinations that reciprocity may become possible, but this we cannot expect for some years. For certain purposes a Dominion Registration Bureau at Ottawa seems specially indicated; thus the surgeon of a Quebec regiment doing duty in Ontario would be practising illegally, and in the marine, the surgeons sailing in the passenger steamers must be registered in the province of the port from which the vessel hails. There would be great if not insuperable objections raised to any such bureau, though it might be feasible to devise a plan for the military surgeons and those belonging to the mercantile marine.[1]

I have dealt thus fully with the constitution and functions of the medical boards of the provinces, because I feel convinced that the safety of the profession rests with them. Of inestimable service in the past, their work in the future will be even more beneficent. Do arouse to a sense of your professional advantages. Where else do the medical men of a country enjoy the rights of conducting their own affairs in their own parliament? Look at Great Britain, where our mighty sister Association, with all her influence, and backed by eleven thousand members, could not force the principle of professional representation into the last medical bill, and at the best was only able to secure three or four members from the profession at large. Rest content, when in each Province of this Dominion you have (1) an elective representative assembly (medical board, council, or college), with members from each teaching body; (2) absolute control of preliminary qualifications, curriculum, and examinations for the license to practise; (3) appropriate accommodation for the meetings of the boards, for the conducting of examinations, and for preservation of the local and general archives of the profession. The full development of the Acts of 1788 and 1815 will not be reached until these things are accomplished. The first two you have already won in a majority of the Provinces, the last will perhaps be the most difficult of accomplishment; but I feel confident that the day is not distant when in the capital of each province the incorporated profession will have a stately Æsculapian temple worthy the traditions and aspirations of our high calling.

And here I may reasonably conclude this portion of my theme, which is concerned particularly with the relations of the profession to the community, but I will dwell upon one point. I began by saying that in a well-ordered State every citizen should feel that he has near at hand well-trained men, to whom in the hour of need he may turn with confidence, and ask aid for himself, his wife, or his little ones. That throughout Canada this condition exists, that the community is to-day served by capable and well-trained men, that within reach of the poorest in our smallest villages there is an honest, capable physician, that imposters and charlatans are few; these, gentlemen, are some of the blessings for which we may, lifting both hands to heaven, thank our Medical Boards.

To another important relation of the medical profession to the community I can but briefly refer. One of the most remarkable developments of modern medicine has been the direction of the study of the causes and mode of prevention of epidemic diseases. The principles of preventive medicine have been gradually receiving due recognition on the part of the public, and the necessity for organized effort is generally acknowledged. In this province the effort has resulted in the establishment of the Provincial Board of Health, which is doing a great work, and should receive the active support of the public and the profession. The successful course which it has pursued during the past four years affords a stimulus which the other provinces must sooner or later feel, and sets an example which for very shame they must follow.

2. The medical school. In the progress and development of a profession, the medical school plays an important and essential part. The primary object is the training of young men in the science and art of medicine, to supply the community with fit and proper persons to take charge of the sick and injured, and it is with this aspect of a medical school that the public is naturally concerned. In most European countries the State, as guardian of the public weal, undertakes the control of medical education and subsidizes largely the medical faculties of the universities. In Great Britain this is also done to a slight extent, but everywhere on this continent the schools have arisen as a result of private enterprise. The origin and evolution of the medical school in this country are quite easy to trace. For many years private tuition was the sole means of obtaining a medical education, and the system of apprenticeship prevailed to a large extent. In a series of "grinds" or "quizzes" the preceptor would take his pupils over the whole range of medicine and surgery, and a knowledge of anatomy was obtained by private dissec-

tion, which was carried on extensively. The office practice and the daily round furnished clinical material. The student was much with his preceptor, became his friend and companion, and in the course of four or five years, sometimes less, grew really very proficient in the practical working of his profession, and felt prepared to present himself before the Provincial Board. Some of the very best practitioners we have had in Canada received their medical education in this way. Take the Medical Register of Ontario or Quebec and seek out the names of the men which have simply Lic. of the Med. Bd. of Upper Canada or of Lower Canada after them, and we find among them many of the men we know best and respect the most highly. Without doubt, in good hands, the old system had great advantages; the essential, useful, and practical details of professional life were well taught; for the refinements and superfluities, the busy physician found no time. Among the private teachers before medical schools became generally accessible, were some notable men whose names deserve to be mentioned in grateful remembrance. Dr. James Douglass, of Quebec, was a remarkably successful as well as popular teacher, and his pupils had the great advantage of the Marine Hospital. He still lives in peaceful retirement, one of the few links uniting the profession of Quebec to a generation long past. The late Dr. Rolph, from the date of his removal to Toronto in 1831 until the foundation of the Toronto School of Medicine in 1843, was one of the most energetic and successful private teachers, and many of his pupils of that date now occupy prominent positions among us. Even after the troublous times of 1837, when he had to cross the border, the students followed him to Rochester.

The organization of the first medical school arose from the association of two or three men engaged in private teaching, who thought that it would be more advantageous, and save time, if each one taught one or two branches. In 1824, at Montreal, Drs. Stephenson, Holmes, Caldwell, and Robertson gave the first definite course of lectures in medicine delivered in this country. This "Medical Institution," as they called it, became, in 1829, the medical faculty of McGill College, and remained for many years the only medical school in the country. The next

attempt was a much more ambitious one. As early as 1835–
efforts were made to induce the government of Sir John Colburn
to establish a faculty of medicine in King's College, Toronto,
and elaborate plans were prepared, but nothing came of it until
1843, when a faculty was organized with a full and able staff.
A more favorable inauguration of a medical school could not
have been devised; with State aid, well-trained and efficient
professors, who were in the receipt of salaries ranging from
£225 to £350—fine emoluments for those days. From all I can
gather, the school was a thoroughly efficient one, and did good
work in medical education, but the professors made certain
mistakes for which they paid heavily. In opposing the incorporation of the Toronto School of Medicine, which had been
organized by Dr. Rolph in 1843, they acted most injudiciously,
laid the foundation of future trouble, and too many of them
were hostile to the profession in their desire for a better medical
act. After an existence of ten years, an act of the Legislature
left the University of Toronto with only the academical department, and swept away a medical school which, whatever
its faults, had in it the elements of ultimate success, and left
the profession and the public at the mercy of irresponsible
schools without foundations and dependent on private enterprise. There can be no doubt that the abolition of the faculty
of medicine of the University of Toronto retarded seriously the
growth of the profession in this country. The establishment of
a well-equipped institution would have been an example and
a stimulus to others, and as years passed, the difficulties inevitably associated with the first few years of existence would
have vanished.

In 1843 the Montreal School of Medicine and Surgery was
founded, and continues as the largest French school in the
Dominion. About the same time the St. Lawrence School was
started in Montreal in opposition to McGill College, but it had
a short life and soon expired. The Quebec School of Medicine
next started and became, and continues as the medical faculty
of Laval University. In Toronto a third school was added to the
existing ones in 1850 by the establishment of the Upper Canada
School of Medicine, which, in its first session, became the med-

ical faculty of Trinity College, and after an existence of three or four sessions, ended by the resignation of the professors who refused to submit to certain vexatious test enactments of a religious nature demanded by the corporation. The faculty of medicine of Victoria College was next established in Toronto, for years known as Rolph's School; it terminated its existence in 1869. The Kingston School, organized as a faculty of Queen's University, is now known as the Royal College of Physicians and Surgeons. The faculty of medicine of Bishop's College, Lennoxville, P.Q., was organized in Montreal in 1870. In the same year the faculty of medicine of Trinity College was reorganized and exists now as a separate corporation known as Trinity Medical School. The Medical School at Halifax is the only one which has been started in the Lower Provinces.

The most recent additions to our list have been the Branch of Laval Medical Faculty at Montreal, 1877; the faculty of medicine of Western University, London, Ont., and the faculty of the University of Manitoba, both organized within the past few years; and in 1883, as the outcome of an unfortunate contretemps at Kingston, a School of Medicine for Women was started in that city, and followed by the establishment of another for the same purpose in Toronto.

Of this latest development, there cannot but be a feeling of regret that our friends in these cities should have entered upon undertakings so needless in this country. It is useless manufacturing articles for which there is no market, and in Canada the people have not yet reached the condition in which the lady doctor finds a suitable environment. Look at the facts as they are; even the larger cities can only support one or two; in fact, Quebec and Montreal have none, and in smaller towns and villages of this country she would starve. For the sake of educating six or eight women annually, of whom at least three or four will go abroad, two more medical schools have been established with full staffs of professors and teachers. We can but hope that at the expiration of the five years for which kind friends have guaranteed the expenses, the promoters of these institutions will be in a position to place their energies and funds at the disposal of the schools devoted to the sterner sex.

Do not understand from these remarks that I am in any hostile to the admission of women to our ranks; on the contrary, my sympathies are entirely with them in the attempt to work out the problem as to how far they can succeed in such an arduous profession as that of medicine.

Exclusive, then, of the schools for women, there are existing eleven teaching bodies throughout the country, three French and eight English, a goodly number to supply the wants of about five millions of people. In Great Britain, with a population of thirty-five millions, there are about 34 medical schools, and in the United States, with a population of fifty millions, there are 139 schools, so that in comparison with these countries we are very abundantly supplied.

The youngest among us may have watched the incubation and birth, and many of us the gradual growth and development of a medical school. With scarcely an exception every one which has started owes its origin to the individual exertions of members of the profession. There are men present who could tell us that the task is not a light one to-day, but what must it have been to those who began the work fifty of sixty years ago? It was an unending struggle against serious obstacles and difficulties. Money had to be raised for buildings and apparatus, and with but few students and small returns, the marvel is not that only four have succumbed in the struggle, but that so many have survived. The internal difficulties are often the most serious; the brunt of the work in such enterprises always falls on one or two zealous men who have to carry the chief part of the load, and the dead weight of lethargic colleagues has been the heaviest burden to many an ardent spirit.

Debt is the millstone which keeps the young schools under for many years; borrowed money furnishes the appliances, etc., and even in the older schools each addition to the buildings means so much more interest to pay. In only one or two of the faculties connected with universities have the governors even furnished suitable accommodations. The financial condition is for years oppressing, and from session to session the school drags on, living from hand to mouth, barely able to meet liabilities and pay the teachers—at this stage most probably not at all. As the number of students increases so do the finances improve, and, if a school proves popular, the debts may be paid off and the professors receive fair remuneration, but, so long as the attendance is limited, the receipts are only such as will barely meet the expenditures. A difficulty which under the present circumstances seems insuperable, is the fact of absolute dependence for success upon the number of students; small classes mean restricted capabilities for teaching, spiritless instruction, low-spirited professors, and general discontent, particularly on the part of the faculty. Large classes mean perhaps the opposite of all this, but not always; still there is a cheeriness about a professor the benches of whose classroom are well filled. I have known a small entry depress for the session the spirits of a man whose estimation of everything was numerical.

Let us glance at the facts as they stand. I estimate that last season there were in the eleven Canadian schools about 900 students, from whom, with trifling exception, the entire support of the institutions was derived. Four of the eleven institutions are greedy enough to attract at least 700 students, leaving about 200 to be divided among the seven other schools. With the low scale of fees at present in vogue, I doubt if each student paid more than an average of $80 per annum for instruction, so that the total receipts at the number of students above mentioned would be about $70,000, of which at least $55,000 goes to four of the schools, leaving a balance of not more than $15,000 to be divided among the remaining seven. Now, a modern school of medicine is a serious affair to undertake and equip; there are branches to be taught which require, even the smallest schools, plenty of room and good apparatus. Laboratories for the practical teaching of chemistry, histology, anatomy, pathology, and physiology must be provided, and arrangements made for library and museum purposes. Personal expenditure on the part of members of the faculty can alone supply these in some of the schools, and in almost all the rule has been that each lecturer from his fees shall provide his own teaching outfit. Where the teacher has enthusiasm and a purse this may work well, and indeed does so sometimes, for I know of an instance of an outlay of over two thousand dollars in apparatus, and of another in which the personal laboratory expenses were always between five hundred and one thousand dollars annually. As matters have been in our schools heretofore, without personal expenditure laboratory equipment has been defective. The remarkable impetus which has been given of late to practical teaching has increased very much the expense of conducting a school, for not only have the laboratories to be provided, but special men must be forthcoming with special training. The general practitioner who has for eight or ten years been busy at practical medicine and surgery may step into the professor's chair and give a good, sensible course of lectures; but to conduct laboratory work demands careful and prolonged training, which costs much money, and when obtained has a market value.

One great evil which results from this condition is the competition for patronage among the schools which I have already alluded to as a danger to be carefully watched by the profession. Too many of the students enter upon the study before they have means sufficient to carry them through the entire course, and they seek special inducements, reduction in fees, exemption from attendance until Christmas, and will often in letters set off one school against another in a most amusing way. Think, gentlemen, to what the unrestricted competition among eleven schools for 900 students might bring the profession! It would be a struggle for existence in which the public and the profession would certainly be the losers, but with the wise regulations already referred to, existing in each province, the competition is reduced to reasonable limits, as all students, irrespective of their schools, must virtually pursue the same plan of study and for the same length of time.

What is the remedy? The small schools have rights equally with the large; they cannot be asked to immolate themselves in the interests of more favored institutions. It is plainly within the duty of the provincial boards to inquire into the equipment of the teaching bodies, and they should refuse recognition to those which have not appliances fit to conduct a modern medical course; or, what would be better still, the medical boards should have the power of prohibiting the establishment of a new school until satisfied that its promoters had money sufficient to begin such an enterprise, and had suitable buildings and hospital accommodation. In the future one of two things will take place: either a considerable number of the small schools will die of starvation—for it is quite evident on the above financial statement, which is approximately correct, that there are seven existing on class fees which could only support one, and that in a not very flourishing manner—or means must be devised to secure funds from other sources. That there are superfluous schools in the country, no one can deny, and the death of three or four under present circumstances would be no loss to the profession or the public; but if all could be furnished with suitable clinical and scientific equipments, they would then prove a source of strength, not of weakness. Dependent solely on class fees, the smaller schools, even with the self-sacrifice of professors which I know of in many instances, cannot hope to keep up with the modern requirements in medical teaching, and the larger schools, with their increased expenses and increased salaries, are really not much better off. The time has come when we should lay clearly before the public the needs of higher medical education. The full development of a school cannot be reached without extraneous aid. To build laboratories and provide costly apparatus require sums quite outside the power of the faculties or the professors to supply. We should learn a lesson from our brethren of the clergy. Ask in Toronto and Montreal the purpose of so many beautiful and costly buildings clustering about the universities of these towns, and we are told they are the divinity schools, in many instances erected at the cost of individual donors. The number of men in this country is rapidly increasing who have money to give where they see it is needed and will be profitably employed; and if those interested in medical education bestir themselves actively, suitable endowment can be obtained. We have not asked before—in careless unconsciousness of our needs—but we must ask now and ask earnestly. The successful appeal for $100,000 made last year in Montreal is at once an indication and an encouragement. There are strong, enlightened men among us, like the Hon. Donald A. Smith, who feel, with Descartes, that the hope of the amelioration of many of the ills of humanity lies within our profession, and that it is a public duty and privilege to assist in making our colleges true seats of learning, as well as schools of sound instruction.

3. The medical society. In a young country the organization of medical societies is associated with serious difficulties. In cities practitioners can easily meet together, but in communities scattered over a wide extent of territory, like Canada, general societies are not readily established. Thus we find that several attempts were made to organize a Canadian Medical Association, but without success until the confederation of the provinces in 1867. In 1845 the Medico-Chirurgical Society of Montreal sought to secure a Provincial Medical Association, and called a conference of delegates from the societies in the city and district of Quebec, and the district of Niagara and Toronto. A meeting of the delegates was held on the 20th of August, but the scheme was unfortunately frustrated. In 1850 the same Society again sought to unite the profession of Canada in a British-American Medical and Surgical Association, and on July 10th, at Three Rivers, a preliminary meeting was held, at which a constitution and short code of by-laws were adopted. Dr. Morin, of Quebec, was elected President, and Dr. Hall, of Montreal, Secretary, and the first general meeting was arranged to take place in Kingston on the second Thursday of May, 1851. I do not know that it was ever held; the journals of the day are silent on the subject.

At the instigation and call of the Quebec Medical Society, a meeting was held at Laval University on October 9, 1867, to consider the advisability of establishing a Canadian Medical Association. The organization was successfully effected, and the first meeting was held in Montreal in 1868 under the Presidency of Doctor, now Sir Charles, Tupper.

Among the objects which the promoters sought to effect by united effort was satisfactory and harmonious medical legislation, and we find that, for the first four sessions the time of the Association was chiefly occupied with the framing of a Dominion medical bill, which ultimately proved an impracticable measure, and was droppd. The subsequent meetings have been devoted to more legitimate topics of discussion, and we have reached a truer conception of the objects of our annual gatherings. We are all agreed, I think, that the highest work which an Association such as ours can undertake is the promotion of the scientific and practical aspects of the profession. To these meetings the best minds among us should bring their best thoughts, that, by reading and discussion of papers, we may be mutually benefited. Every member can bring something. One great attraction in our profession is its freshness and novelty. Each one of us has had, since our last meeting, opportunities for the study of problems in disease, new, perhaps unexpected, and which may not occur to us again. Material for original work and research lies in the daily round of each one, awaiting only the spirit of patient and earnest inquiry, lacking which we cannot wonder that men deem the practice of medicine dull, stale, and flat. Every one should come to learn, and of necessity brings with him something he can teach, for in certain points his experience supplements what is wanting in another's. To our gatherings all teachers in our schools should come to meet their brethren and give to them an account of their stewardship—for do they not hold their positions in trust?—and show by their work and ways that they merit the confidence reposed in them. The more we foster the scientific features of our gatherings, the more successful will the Association be. It has been so with our sister associations in Great Britain, and in France and Germany the corresponding societies form sections of the general associations for the advancement of science, and the meetings are devoted exclusively to work.

By no means the smallest advantage of our meetings is the promotion of harmony and good-fellowship. Medical men, particularly in smaller places, live too much apart and do not see enough of each other. In large cities we rub each other's angles down and carrom off each other without feeling the shock very much, but it is an unfortunate circumstance that in many town the friction, being on a small surface, hurts; and mutual misunderstandings arise to the destruction of all harmony. As a result of this may come a professional isolation with a corroding influence of a most disastrous nature, converting, in a few years, a genial, good fellow into a bitter old Timon, railing against the practice of medicine in general, and his colleagues in particular. As a preventative of such a malady attendance upon our annual gatherings is absolute, as a cure it is specific. But I need not dwell on this point—he must indeed be a stranger in such meetings as ours who has not felt the glow of sympathy and affection as the hand of a brother worker has been grasped in kindly fellowship.

There is a special need in this country for such an association. With scattered and isolated provinces, self-governing, and regulating their own affairs, this organization is the sole bond of professional union. At these meetings we are neither of Ontario nor Quebec, of Manitoba nor Nova Scotia, but of Canada, and the narrower provincial spirit is lost in a wider national feeling. In the future development of the profession this body must take an ever-increasing share. It has difficulties to contend with of a geographical nature, as the distances between our provinces are so great, but these must not be considered. A peripatetic association always labors under certain disadvantages, but these we have in common with similar bodies in other countries. The provincial medical societies which have been established, supplement the work which we do and are a source of strength. We regret that there are still one or two provinces without such organizations. The district societies throughout the country are becoming more and more vigorous, and physicians are everywhere recognizing the advantage of cooperation in the study of our profession.

Let me refer to two other matters in conclusion. In selecting the place of meeting the Association should be guided by what is thought best for the interests of the profession, and it should be distinctly understood that when we meet at any place the sole business of the local profession is to arrange suitable accommodation; and this Association must set itself strongly against past practices by which the profession of a place has been heavily taxed for entertainment. In this we should follow the custom of the British Medical Association, at the meetings of which all the members subscribe to the association dinner; and I should ask for the reappointment of the committee to revise the by-laws and constitution, as there are certain changes which will facilitate the work of our meetings and which should be brought up for discussion at as early a date as possible.

And now, gentlemen, I have done, and there remains but the expression of my thanks for the kind attention you have given to a very matter-of-fact address, but I cannot part with you on this occasion without assuring through you, my brethren in Canada that, although no longer of them, I am still with them in spirit, with them in their persistent efforts to advance the higher interests of our profession, and united with them by a thousand bonds of fellowship and friendship, which absence shall not weaken nor time efface.

---

[1] Ultimately, through the work of Thomas G. Roddick (1846–1923), the Canada Medical Act was passed by Parliament and approved by all provinces, thus enabling the establishment of the Medical Council of Canada in 1912. Those passing its examination earn the right to registration in any province without further examination. [C.G.R.]

Osler at work

THE HISTORICAL DEVELOPMENT AND RELATIVE VALUE OF LABORATORY AND CLINICAL METHODS IN DIAGNOSIS.

THE EVOLUTION OF THE IDEA OF EXPERIMENT IN MEDICINE

The Transactions of the Congress of American Physicians and Surgeons *published Osler's "The Historical Development and Relative Value of Laboratory and Clinical Methods in Diagnosis: The Evolution of the Idea of Experiment in Medicine"* in 1907 (vol. 7, pages 1–8).

THAT man can interrogate as well as observe nature was a lesson slowly learned in his evolution. Of the two methods by which he can do this, the mathematical and the experimental, both have been equally fruitful—by the one he has gauged the starry heights and harnessed the cosmic forces to his will; by the other he has solved many of the problems of life and lightened many of the burdens of humanity.

Of the beginnings of experimental science we have no accurate knowledge, but the men who invented the gnomon and predicted ellipses on the plains of Mesopotamia, that mysterious Sumerian race, laid its foundation, and their knowledge became a powerful instrument in the hands of the Ionian nature-philosopher, of whom Thales is the venerable head. Great thinkers, and with magical instinct, these old Greeks had anticipations of nearly every modern discovery, but we have details of one really fundamental experiment, and that was when Pythagoras discovered the dependence of the pitch of sound on the length of the vibrating chord. "The monochord which he used for his experiments on the physics of sound consisted of a string stretched over a resounding board with a movable bridge, by means of which it was possible to divide the strings into different lengths, and thus to produce the various high and low notes on one and the same string."

Had the Greeks added to their genius for brilliant generalization and careful observation the capacity to design and carry out experiments, the history of European thought would have been very different, but neither Plato nor Aristotle had any conception of the value of experiment as an instrument in the progress of knowledge. Hippocrates appreciated the *fact* as an essential element more highly than any of his contemporaries, and though he had theoretical conceptions of disease, yet to him facts, as obtained by observation, were the Alpha and Omega of the art. To seek for facts by altering the conditions which nature presented did not occur to him, and yet it must over and over again have happened in the treatment of fractures that he had to try new methods and devise new procedures; and to shake a man with fluid in his chest to get what we call the Hippocratic succession was a noteworthy clinical experiment.

With the great masters of the Alexandrine school, time has dealt hardly. Had we their complete works we should find that they were not only the first great anatomists, but that to clinical acumen of an extraordinary quality was added a zeal for experimentation, which, if Celsius is to be credited, led to the vivisection of criminals. Like his teacher, Praxagoras, Herophilus made the state of the pulse the measure of the strength of the constitution, and timed it with a water-clock, but both to him and to Erasistratos we owe more anatomical and clinical than physiological observations. They extended the Hippocratic art of observation to the dead house and were the first to see the value of morbid anatomy.

Among the dogmatics and empirics arose the science of toxicology and the study of poisons and their antidotes led to an active cultivation of this side of experimental medicine. Not only animals, but criminals were used to test the effects of poisons, and the art reached its climax in antiquity in the royal student, Mithradates, who could to-day talk intelligently with Ehrlich about immunity, in which he had grasped two fundamental facts—the conference of protection by gradually increasing the dosage of the poison, and the use of the blood of animals rendered immune. What an interested visitor he would be to-day in a diphtheria antitoxine laboratory, in which he could compare the methods in use in the horse with those which he employed for his ducks. The name of the great king was embalmed in the profession for nearly two thousand years in the universal antidote, Mithradaticon, with 50 to 60 ingredients.

One man alone among the ancients could walk into the physiological laboratories to-day and feel at home. Claudius Galen was not a greater observer than Hippocrates, nor perhaps a greater anatomist than Herophilus or Erasistratos, nor was he so brilliant and daring a surgeon as Antyllus, but he stands out in our history as the first physician who had a clear conception of medicine as a science. He recognized that valuable as observation was, the bare fact was not science, but only the preliminary, the first step towards that organized grouping of facts from which principles and laws could be derived. Not structure alone, with which anatomy is satisfied, but function, the use of the part, was to be ascertained; not the symptom of the disease alone was to be investigated, but the cause, how it arose. In brilliant experiments upon the heart and arteries he almost demonstrated the circulation of the blood; in his work on the nervous system he anticipated the discoveries of Bell and Marshall Hall, and he laid the foundations for our knowledge of the physiology of the brain and spinal cord.

For long centuries the anatomy, the physiology, the surgery and the practice of Galen dominated the schools—Byzantine, Arabic, Salernitan all bowed in humble, slavish submission to his authority, taking from him everything but his spirit, everything but the new instrument which he had put into the hands of the profession. Valuable observations were added, and the middle ages were perhaps not as barren as we are taught to believe, but there was nowhere any attempt to take up the experimental work which had so auspiciously begun. Still a brilliant torch was lighted by the Arabians from the lamps of Aristotle and Galen, and in the first Greek Renaissance between the 8th and 11th centuries the profession reached, among them, a position of dignity and importance to which it is hard to find a parallel in its history. The foundations of modern chemistry were laid, and many new drugs were added to the pharmacopeia, but though Rhazes was known as the experimentator, neither in his writings nor in those of other men of the Arabian school do we find any solid contribution to anatomy or physiology. Nor did the second Greek Renaissance, at the end of the 15th century, at once bring relief. Men were too busy scraping off the Arabian tarnish from the pure gold of Greek medicine, and correcting the mistakes of Galen in anatomy, to bother about disturbing his physiology or pathology. Here and there among the great anatomists of the period we read of an experiment, but it was the art of observation, the art of Hippocrates, not the science of Galen, not the carefully devised experiment to determine function, that characterized their work. There was indeed every reason why men should have been content with the physiology and pathology of that day, as from a theoretical standpoint it was excellent. The doctrine of the four humors and of the natural, animal and vital spirit afforded a ready explanation for the symptoms of all diseases, and the practice of the day was admirably adapted to the theories. There was no thought of, no desire for change. But the revival of learning awakened in men at first a suspicion and at last a conviction that the ancients had left something which could be reached by independent research, and gradually the paralytic-like torpor passed away. Independent spirits like Paracelsus defied all academic traditions and threw the doctrines of Galen and Avicenna to the winds. But throughout the 16th century there was very little experimental work in medicine, and though Paracelsus and his followers made researches in chemistry and improved the art of pharmacy, it was still the age of the eye and the devising hand, as an instrument of the mind had not yet been called into requisition. Astronomy, which had given science the start originally, again gave it the needed stimulus, and the inventions and discoveries of Copernicus, Kepler and Galileo revived mechanical invention and experimentation in medicine. At our second Congress, you remember how graphically Dr. Weir Mitchell told the story of instrumental precision in medicine. An important part of this address was taken up with an account of Sanctorius and his construction of the thermometer and the pulsilogum of Galileo and the balance. Nothing can be added to Dr. Mitchell's account of the experimental and clinical work of Sanctorius; indeed it is the only complete account in English, and, as he pointed out, in the investigations of this Italian physician we have the beginnings of our clinical and experimental work in the physics of the circulation and respiration and in metabolism. The memory of the great investigator has not been helped by the English edition of the aphorisms, which is a feeble work, with the picture of the author in his dietetic balance, and we must turn to the originals or to Dr. Mitchell's address to appreciate that with him the science of medicine takes a new start in aiding observation with instruments of precision.

Contemporaneously with Sanctorius, Harvey was quietly working at the problem of the circulation of the blood and perfecting through a series of years his remarkable demonstrations. It is interesting that his method of work was a new departure, and showed a new spirit. We have to go back to Galen and his hemi-section of the spinal cord or to his division of the recurrent laryngial nerve for similar studies on function deliberately planned and deliberately carried out by way of experiment.

Neither Sanctorius nor Harvey had the immediate influence upon their contemporaries which the novel and stimulating character of their work justified. Harvey's great countryman, Bacon, although he lost his life in making a cold storage experiment, did not really appreciate the enormous importance of experimental science. It was a philosopher of another kidney, René Descartes, who did more than anyone to help men to realize the value of the better way which Harvey had pointed out. That the beginning of wisdom was in doubt, not in authority, was a novel doctrine in the world, but he was no armchair philosopher, and his strong advocacy and practice of experimentation had a profound influence in directing man to *la nouvelle methode*. He brought the human body, the earthly machine, as he calls it, into the sphere of mechanics and physics, and he wrote the first text-book of physiology, *De l'homme*. Locke, too, became the spokesman of the new questioning spirit, and before the close of the 17th century experimental research became all the mode, and Evelyn tells us that the Merry Monarch had a laboratory and knew many of the empirical medicines. Lower, Hooke and Hales were probably more influenced by Descartes than by Harvey, and they made noteworthy contributions to experimental physiology in England. Borelli brought to the study of the action of muscles a profound knowledge of physics and mathematics and really founded the iatro-mathematical school.

Modern experimental chemistry had its origin in the alchemy of the Arabians, and we can trace its progress through Basil, Valentine, Paracelsus, van Helmont, Boyle and Sylvius. Mayow, in a brilliant series of researches, solved the problem of combustion, and demonstrated the essential part played in respiration by the nitro-aerial part (the oxygen as we now know it) of the air.

In the latter half of the eighteenth century experimental science received an enormous impetus through the work of two men. Spallanzani demonstrated the chemical nature of the digestive process, and from him dates our modern science of reproduction. In John Hunter there met a rare triple combination—powers of observation which in width and acuteness have rarely been equalled, a perfect genius for experimentation, and such a philosophic grasp of the problems of disease as enabled him to raise pathology into a science. To his student and friend, Edward Jenner, we owe the great experiments from which date our practical work on immunity.

In the beginning of the last century the art of observation, the great instrument of Hippocrates, found the full development in the hands of the French school, by which the diagnosis of disease was put upon a sound basis, while in the forties the keen eyes of Virchow revealed to us for the first time the true seats of disease. The work of Bichat, of Laennec, of Louis, and the monumental studies of the great Berlin pathologist, illustrated what the rigid inductive method could accomplish by minds freed from all dominating theories under the control of the law of facts, and no longer trafficking in hypotheses. But the century was well advanced before the profession realized the full worth of the method of Galen, of Harvey and of Hunter. How slow we were to appreciate this is illustrated by what Helmholtz tells of the celebrated professor of physiology in the fifties, who, asked to see an experiment in optics, said, "A physiologist has nothing to do with experiments, though they might be well enough for a physicist!" The last half of the century may be called the era of experimental medicine, and the truly prodigious results have been along three lines—the discovery of the functions of organs, the discovery of the causes of disease and the discovery of new methods of treatment. A single generation, indeed, has witnessed a complete readjustment of our outlook on physiology, pathology, and practice, and all this has come from a recognition that experiment is the very basis of science. Much has been done, but when we look ahead at what remains we see that only a beginning has been made, and there is not a department in practical medicine in which there are not innumerable problems of the first rank awaiting solution. And every new advance in physiology demands from the pathologist and clinician a change of view and a reopening of old questions believed to be settled. Such work as that of Starling's on the correlation of secretions has already opened a new field for observation and research. With the advances in physics and chemistry it becomes increasingly difficult to find men with the training necessary to attack intelligently these complicated problems. We need in association with all our large hospitals clinical laboratories in charge of men who will be selected to do this work by directors who are themselves thinkers as well as workers. For often all the essence of a successful experiment is the thought that precedes it. *Deviner avant de démonstrator* must be the motto of every experimental investigator. We must have clinicians who keep in close touch with physiology, pathology and chemistry, and who are prepared to transfer to the wards through proper channels the knowledge of the laboratory. The organized medical clinic is a clearinghouse for the scientific traders who are doing business in all parts of the body corporate, and the application of new facts to medicine must come through it, or through that small but happily increasing group of men who find time amid the daily cares of practice. One thing is certain; we clinicians must go to the physiologists, the pathologists and the chemists—they no longer come to us. To our irreparable loss these sciences have become so complicated and demand such life-long devotion that no longer do physiologists, like Hunter, Bowman and Lister, become surgeons, chemists, like Prout and Bence-Jones, clinicians, and saddest of all, the chair of pathology is no longer a stepping-stone to the chair of medicine. The new conditions must be met if progress is to be maintained. In every country there will be found strong men, like Weir Mitchell, Mackenzie of Barnley, and Meltzer and Christian Herter, who find it possible to combine experimental work with practice, but we must recognize the pressing need of organization if internal medicine is to keep in close touch with the rapid advancement of the sciences. A glance at the program of the Association of American Physicians' meeting indicates the dominance of experiment at the present day.

To each one of us life is an experiment in Nature's laboratory, and she tests and tries us in a thousand ways, using and improving us if we serve her turn, ruthlessly dispensing with us if we do not. Disease is an experiment, and the earthly machine is a culture medium, a test tube and a retort—the external agents, the medium and the reaction constituting the factors. We constantly experiment with ourselves in food and drink, and the expression so often on our lips, "Does it agree with you?" signifies how tentative are many of our daily actions. The treatment of disease has always been experimental, and started indeed in these haphazard endeavors of friends and relatives to try something to help the sufferer. Each dose of medicine given is an experiment, as it is impossible to predict in every instance what the result may be. Thousands of five-grain doses of iodide of potassium may be given without ill effect, and then conditions are met with in which the patient reacts with an outbreak of purpura, or a fatal result may follow. A deviation from what we had regarded as a settled rule, a break in a sequence thought to be invariable, emphasizes the impossibility of framing general rules for the body of the same rigid applicability as in physics and mechanics. The limits of justifiable experimentation upon our fellow creatures are well and clearly defined. The final test of every new procedure, medical or surgical must be made on man, but never before it has been tried on animals. There are those who look upon this as unlawful, but in no other way is progress possible, nor could we have had many of our most useful but very powerful drugs if animal experimentation had been forbidden. For man absolute safety and full consent are the conditions which make such tests allowable. We have no right to use patients entrusted to our care for the purpose of experimentation unless direct benefit to the individual is likely to follow. Once this limit is transgressed, the sacred cord which binds physician and patient snaps instantly. Risk to the individual may be taken with his consent and full knowledge of the circumstances, as has been done in scores of cases, and we cannot honor too highly the bravery of such men as the soldiers who voluntarily submitted to the experiments on yellow fever in Cuba under the direction of Reed and Carroll. The history of our profession is starred with the heroism of its members who have sacrificed health and sometimes life itself in endeavors to benefit their fellow creatures. Enthusiasm for science has, in a few instances, led to regrettable transgressions of the rule I have mentioned, but these are mere specks which in no wise blur the brightness of the picture—one of the brightest in the history of human effort—which portrays the incalculable benefits to man from the introduction of experimentation into the art of medicine.

A NOTE ON THE TEACHING OF THE HISTORY OF MEDICINE

This note was published originally as a letter-to-the-editor of the British Medical Journal *(Vol. 2) page 93, July 12, 1902.*

IN connexion with the discussion on this subject which has taken place in the columns of the *British Medical Journal,* a brief statement of the methods adopted in the Johns Hopkins Medical School may be of interest.

1. *Lectures.*—Since the opening of the hospital in 1889, Dr. John S. Billings has held the position of Lecturer on the History of Medicine, and has given an annual course, attendance upon which is optional.

2. *The Historical Club.*—Organized in 1889, a monthly meeting is held throughout the winter sesion. During the first three years an attempt was made to cover systematically the great epochs. Dr. Welch dealt very fully with the Alexandrian and Arabian Schools, and one evening was devoted to an exhibition of the chief works on the History of Medicine. Dr. Kelly has repeatedly brought out treasures of his private collection, and has contributed many papers to the history of obstetrics and gynaecology. The volumes of the *Hospital Bulletin* contain about a dozen articles read before the Club, some of which have had the honour of a notice in the *Journal.* Altogether the Club has been successful, not only in stimulating interest in the subject, but as a routine means of education.

From the personal collection of C.G. Roland

William Osler

3. In the everyday work of the wards, and of the out-patient department the student may be helped to get into the habit of looking at a subject from the historical standpoint. In my out-patient class this is made a special feature of the teaching. A case of exopthalmic goître comes in—the question at once is put, Who was Graves? Who was Parry? Who was Basedow? Of course the student does not know; he is told to bring, on

another day, the original article, and he is given five or ten minutes in which to read a brief historical note. I take from the class-book at random the titles of some subjects which have been presented this session, very often to the edification of the teachers as much as the students: Sydenham's description of chorea, Valsalva's method of treating aneurysm, Tufnell's method of treating aneurysm, the history of our knowledge of lead-poisoning, Abram Colles and his law, Dr. King's safety valve action of the tricuspid valve, Bright's original description of the disease which bears his name, Glisson's original description of rickets, Blaud and his pill, the history of haemophilia in America, the history of diabetes.

4. Once a week, over a little "beer and baccy," I meet my clinical clerks in an informal conference upon the events of the week. For half an hour I give a short talk on one of the "Masters of Medicine," in which, as far as possible, the original editions of the works are shown.

In the present crowded state of the curriculum it does not seem desirable to add the "History of Medicine" as a compulsory subject. An attractive course will catch the good men and do them good, but much more valuable is it to train insensibly the mind of the student into the habit of looking at things from the historical standpoint, which can be done by individual teachers who themselves appreciate the truth of Fuller's remark:

"History maketh a young man to be old, without either wrinkles or grey hairs; privileging him with the experience of age, without either the infirmities or inconveniences thereof. Yea, it not onely maketh things past present, but inableth one to make a rationall conjecture of things to come. For this world affordeth no new accidents, but in the same sense wherein we call it *a new Moon,* which is the old one in another shape, and yet no other then what hath been formerly. Old actions return again, furbished over with some new and different circumstances."

Postscript

This selection of seven items from a total bibliography of over 1500 may be an arbitrary and perhaps unrepresentative sample of Osler's thoughts. Nevertheless, even these few articles demonstrate much about one of our great predecessors. It is hoped that this brief anthology may provide Canadian medical students with an entrée towards an understanding of the breadth of Sir William Osler, and the scope of his life and his work.

C.G.R.

Selected Bibliography

Harvey Cushing: *The Life Of Sir William Osler*, 2 volumes, Oxford,
                    The Clarendon Press, 1925.
                    This intricate biography was awarded the Pu-
                    litzer Prize soon after publication. It remains in
                    print, the classic account of Osler's remarkable
                    career.

Edith Gittings Reid: *The Great Physician*, London, New York and To-
                    ronto, Oxford University Press, 1931.
                    A much shorter and less scholarly biography
                    that is nevertheless accurate and sympathetic.

Anne Wilkinson: *Lions in the Way: A Discursive History of the Oslers*,
                    Toronto, The Macmillan Company of Canada,
                    Ltd., 1956.
                    Lions in the Way is a short and eminently read-
                    able account of the entire remarkable Osler fam-
                    ily, written by a descendant.

Maude Abbott: *Classified and Annotated Bibliography of Sir William
                    Osler's Publications*, Montreal, McGill University,
                    1939.
                    Although a few additional items have been
                    brought to light since Maude Abbott published
                    her bibliography, this is the only substantive
                    work on the topic.

Earl F. Nation,   *An Annotated Checklist of Osleriana*, Kent State
Charles G. Roland & University Press, 1976.
John P. McGovern: This annotated bibliography gives access to
                    the greater part of the mass of material written
                    about Sir William over the past six or seven dec-
                    ades. Its organization is chronological and there
                    is an index.